Electrical and Electronic Principles for Technicians

Electrical and Electronic Principles for Technicians Volume 1

D C Green
MTech, CEng, MIEE

Longman Scientific & Technical,
Longman Group UK Limited,
Longman House, Burnt Mill, Harlow,
Essex CM20 2JE, England
and Associated Companies throughout the world.

First published 1992

British Library Cataloguing in Publication Data
  Green, D.C.
    Electrical and electronic principles for
    technicians: Vol 1.
    I. Title
    621.31

    ISBN 0-582-08054-1

Set in Compugraphic Times 10/12 pt.

Printed in Malaysia
by The Commercial Press Sdn. Bhd.,
Serdang Raya, Selangor Darul Ehsan

Contents

Preface

The Business and Technician Education Council (BTEC) programmes in electrical engineering make *Electrical and Electronic Principles* mandatory study at both Levels II and III for all students of Electrical and Electronic Engineering, Electronic Engineering, Communication Engineering, and Computer Engineering. Some other courses, e.g., motor vehicle, may only require Electrical Principles study at Level II. This book has been written to cover the Level II part of the BTEC bank for Electrical Principles.

Throughout preferred values of resistors and capacitors have been employed and most calculations have been rounded off to two places of decimals. This has been done to give the reader a feel of the component values commonly met with in electrical circuitry and to emphasize that very exact calculations are somewhat meaningless when the component values used are subject to tolerances of up to 10% for resistors and even more for capacitors.

The book has been written on the assumption that the reader will have studied or will be concurrently studying mathematics to the BTEC Level II standard. A large number of worked examples are provided throughout the book and exercises on the content of each chapter are to be found at the back of the book. Concise solutions to each numerical exercise are also given.

DCG

1 Circuit theory

There are many instances in electrical and electronic engineering when it is necessary to be able to determine the currents that flow in a circuit when a voltage is applied to the circuit. If the circuit is purely resistive, and all the resistances are *linear*, the calculations can be carried out using Ohm's law. This law states that 'the current flowing in a circuit is directly proportional to the applied voltage and indirectly proportional to the circuit resistance', i.e.,

$$I = V/R \tag{1.1}$$

If the applied voltage is in volts and the circuit resistance is in ohms the current will be in amperes. It is assumed that the resistance is linear; this means that the resistance does not change if the magnitude of the current flowing through it should vary. Non-linear resistances do exist and they are often employed in electronic circuits but the calculation of the current that flows as the result of an applied voltage is much more difficult and beyond the scope of this book.

Very often, particularly in electronic circuits, the currents flowing are small and the milliamp (mA), the microamp (μA), and, less often, the nanoamp (nA) are employed. The milliamp is one-thousandth, and the microamp is one-millionth of an ampere. The nanoamp is one thousandth of a microamp.

Resistors in electronic circuits most often have values of some thousands or even millions of ohms. The prefixes kilo and mega are then used; thus the kilohm (kΩ) is one thousand ohms and the megohm (MΩ) is one million ohms. Resistors are manufactured in standard *preferred* values in each decade of resistance for various percentage resistance tolerances. For example, a 10% 1 kΩ resistor would have a resistance value somewhere in the range 1000 ± 100 ohms, or 900 to 1100 ohms. The standard values for 5%, 10% and 20% tolerance resistors are given in Table 1.1; 1% and 2% tolerance resistors are also available but since the cost of a resistor goes up as its tolerance is made closer (smaller) these resistors are only employed in critical circuits.

Example 1.1

Calculate the possible resistance range of a 39 kΩ resistor.

Table 1.1

20%	10%	5%	20%	20%	20%	20%	20%
10	10	10	100	1 kΩ	10 kΩ	100 kΩ	1 MΩ
		11					
	12	12					
		13					
15	15	15	150	1.5 kΩ	15 kΩ	150 kΩ	1.5 MΩ
		16					
	18	18					
		20					
22	22	22	220	2.2 kΩ	22 kΩ	220 kΩ	2.2 MΩ
		24					
	27	27					
		30					
33	33	33	330	3.3 kΩ	33 kΩ	330 kΩ	3.3 MΩ
		36					
	39	39					
		43					
47	47	47	470	4.7 kΩ	47 kΩ	470 kΩ	4.7 MΩ
		51					
	56	56					
		62					
68	68	68	680	6.8 kΩ	68 kΩ	680 kΩ	6.8 MΩ
		75					
	82	82					
		91					

Solution
From Table 1.1 the resistor may be of either 5% or 10% tolerance.

Five per cent tolerance of 39 kΩ is 1950 Ω, so the resistance value will be somewhere in the range 39 000−1950 or 37.05 kΩ, to 39 000 + 1950 or 40.95 kΩ.   (*Ans.*)

Ten per cent tolerance of 39 kΩ is 3.9 kΩ so the resistance may vary from 35.1 kΩ to 42.9 kΩ.   (*Ans.*)

Because quoted resistance values are all nominal values and the actual resistance may vary either above, or below, the nominal value there is little point in giving the results of calculations to several places of decimals. Therefore, in this book most calculations have been rounded off to two decimal places.

The reader should already possess a knowledge of both Ohm's law and electrical energy and power and should be able to solve simple series and parallel electrical circuits. In this chapter the more complex series—parallel circuits will be considered and these will be solved either by the direct application of Ohm's law or by the use of Kirchhoff's law and its alternatives.

Resistances in series and in parallel

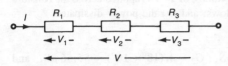

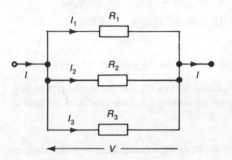

Fig. 1.1 Resistors in series

Fig. 1.2 Resistors in parallel

Figure 1.1 shows three resistors R_1, R_2, and R_3 connected in series. If a voltage V is applied across the circuit a current I will flow which in a series circuit must be the same at all points. By Ohm's law the voltages dropped across each resistor are $V_1 = IR_1$, $V_2 = IR_2$, and $V_3 = IR_3$. The total voltage across the resistors, which is equal to the applied voltage V, must then be $V = V_1 + V_2 + V_3 = I(R_1 + R_2 + R_3)$ and

$$V/I = R_s = R_1 + R_2 + R_3 \qquad (1.2)$$

Thus the total resistance of several resistances connected in series is equal to the algebraic sum of their individual resistance values.

When two, or more, resistors are connected in parallel as in Fig. 1.2 the paralleled resistors have the same voltage V applied across them. The current flowing in each resistor is then equal to this common voltage divided by the resistance of that resistor. Thus, the current I_1 in resistor R_1 is $I_1 = V/R_1$; also $I_2 = V/R_2$, and $I_3 = V/R_3$.

The total current I flowing into, and out of, the parallel resistors is the sum of the individual currents, i.e.,

$$I = I_1 + I_2 + I_3 = V (1/R_1 + 1/R_2 + 1/R_3)$$

and

$$I/V = 1/R_p = 1/R_1 + 1/R_2 + 1/R_3 \qquad (1.3)$$

Thus the reciprocal of the effective resistance of three resistors connected in parallel is equal to the sum of the reciprocals of their individual resistances. The effective resistance will always be smaller than the resistance of the lowest valued of the paralleled resistors.

When there are only two resistors connected in parallel a more convenient expression can be obtained.

$$1/R_p = 1/R_1 + 1/R_2 = (R_1 + R_2)/R_1R_2$$

or $\quad R_p = R_1R_2/(R_1 + R_2) \qquad (1.4)$

Conductance

When dealing with resistors in parallel it is often more convenient to work with the reciprocal of resistance. This is known as conductance. The conductance G, in siemens (S), of a resistor is equal to $1/R$ where R is the resistance of the component. Then the effective conductance of three resistors R_1, R_2 and R_3 connected in parallel is

$$G_p = G_1 + G_2 + G_3 \qquad (1.5)$$

If the applied voltage is V then the total current flowing into, and out of, the circuit is equal to VG and the current in, say, resistor R_2 is VG_2.

Example 1.2

Three resistors of 15 kΩ, 18 kΩ and 22 kΩ are connected in parallel. Calculate their effective conductance. If a voltage of 24 V is applied across the resistors calculate (*a*) the current that flows, and (*b*) the power dissipated.

Solution

$G_1 = 1/(15 \times 10^3) = 66.67\ \mu S$, $G_2 = 1/(18 \times 10^3) = 55.56\ \mu S$, and $G_3 = 1/(22 \times 10^3) = 45.46\ \mu S$. The total effective conductance is $66.67 + 55.56 + 45.46 = 167.69\ \mu S$.

$$I = VG = 24 \times 167.69 \times 10^{-6} = 4.03\ \text{mA}. \quad (Ans.)$$

$$P = IV = 24 \times 4.03 \times 10^{-3} = 96.72\ \text{mW}. \quad (Ans.)$$

Alternatively,

$$P = V^2 G = 24^2 \times 167.69 \times 10^{-6} = 96.59\ \text{mW}. \quad (Ans.)$$

The slight difference in the calculated values for the dissipated power has arisen because of the rounding-off of numbers to two places of decimals.

Series–parallel resistive circuits

In practice, many circuits are more complicated than just the simple series or parallel connection of a number of resistors. Many varied combinations of both series- and parallel-connected resistors are commonly met and the procedures to be adopted to solve such circuits will be illustrated with a number of examples.

Example 1.3

When a voltage is applied across the terminals AB of the circuit given in Fig. 1.3, 10 V are dropped across the 10 kΩ resistor. Calculate (*a*) the applied voltage, and (*b*) the current that flows in the 8.2 kΩ resistor.

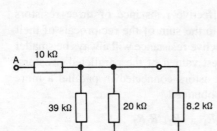

Fig. 1.3

Solution

(*a*) The effective resistance of the three parallel resistors is, working in kΩ, $1/R_p = 1/39 + 1/20 + 1/8.2$, or $R_p = 5.06$ kΩ. The current flowing into the circuit is equal to $10/(10 \times 10^3) = 1$ mA and so the voltage drop across the parallel resistors is $1 \times 10^{-3} \times 5.06 \times 10^3 = 5.06$ V. The applied voltage is $10 + 5.06 \simeq 15$ V.   (*Ans.*)

(*b*) The current in the 8.2 kΩ resistor $= 5.06/(8.2 \times 10^3) = 0.62$ mA.   (*Ans.*)

Alternatively, working in conductances.

(*a*) Conductance of 39 kΩ resistor $= 1/(39 \times 10^3) = 25.64\ \mu S$.
Conductance of 20 kΩ resistor $= 1/(20 \times 10^3) = 50\ \mu S$.
Conductance of 8.2 kΩ resistor $= 1/(8.2 \times 10^3) = 121.95\ \mu S$.
Total conductance $= 25.64 + 50 + 121.95 = 197.59\ \mu S$.
Conductance of 10 kΩ resistor $= 1/(10 \times 10^3) = 100\ \mu S$ and the input current $= VG = 10 \times 100 \times 10^{-6} = 1$ mA.
Voltage across the parallel branch $= I/G = (1 \times 10^{-3})/(197.59 \times 10^{-6}) = 5.06$ V. So, as before, the applied voltage $= 15$ V.   (*Ans.*)

(b) Current in 8.2 kΩ resistor = $VG = 5.06 \times 121.95 \times 10^{-6} =$
0.62 mA.   (Ans.)

Clearly, not much, if anything, has been gained by working in conductances in this instance but sometimes some simplification of the work involved is obtained.

Example 1.4

Calculate the value of the resistor R_1 in Fig. 1.4 if the total resistance of the circuit is 25.32 kΩ.

Solution
Total resistance of the parallel branch = $25.32 - 10 = 15.32$ kΩ. Therefore, working in kΩ, $15.32 = 18(56 + R_1)/(18 + 56 + R_1)$
$15.32 = (1008 + 18R_1)/(74 + R_1)$, $1133.68 + 15.32R_1 = 1008 + 18R_1$
$2.68R_1 = 125.68$ or $R_1 = 47$ kΩ.   (Ans.)

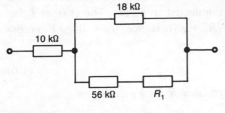

Fig. 1.4

Example 1.5

Calculate the total resistance of the circuit in Fig. 1.5 and the voltage V applied to the circuit.

Solution
Working in kΩ,
$R_s = 5.6 + (25 \times 22)/(25 + 22) + (5.6 \times 33)/(5.6 + 33)$
$\quad = 5.6 + 11.7 + 4.79 = 22.09$ kΩ.   (Ans.)
Voltage across the 33 kΩ resistor = $0.12 \times 10^{-3} \times 33 \times 10^3$
$= 3.96$ V.
Current in the 5.6 kΩ resistor = $3.96/(5.6 \times 10^3) = 0.71$ mA.
Total current = $0.12 + 0.71 = 0.83$ mA. Therefore,
the supply voltage = $0.83 \times 10^{-3} \times 22.09 \times 10^3$
$\qquad\qquad\qquad = 18.34 \simeq 18$ V.   (Ans.)

Voltage and current ratios

The need often arises during calculations on an electric circuit to determine how an applied voltage divides between two, or more, series-connected resistors, or how a current splits between two, or

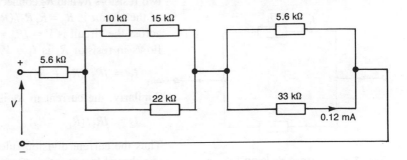

Fig. 1.5

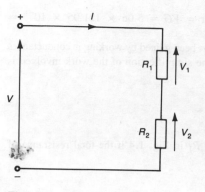

Fig. 1.6 Voltage division

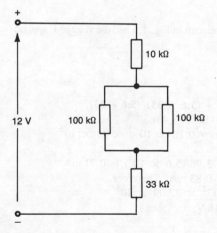

Fig. 1.7

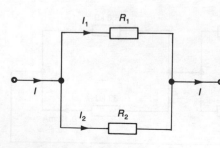

Fig. 1.8 Current division

more, parallel-connected resistors. The required division can always be worked out by the application of Ohm's law but it will generally prove quicker, and more convenient, to employ a simple formula.

Voltage division

Figure 1.6 shows a voltage V applied to a simple circuit that consists of two resistors R_1 and R_2 connected in series. The current I that flows in the circuit is $I = V/(R_1 + R_2)$. Hence, the voltage V_1 across resistor R_1 is $V_1 = IR_1$ or

$$V_1 = VR_1/(R_1 + R_2) \tag{1.6}$$

Also the voltage V_2 across resistor R_2 is $V_2 = IR_2$ or

$$V_2 = VR_2/(R_1 + R_2) \tag{1.7}$$

Thus the voltage division rule is: to determine the voltage across either of two series resistors divide the total applied voltage by the sum of the resistances and multiply by the resistance of the resistor across which the voltage is to be determined. The principle of voltage division can be readily extended to more complex circuits.

Example 1.6

Calculate the voltage across the 100 kΩ resistors in the circuit shown by Fig. 1.7.

Solution

The effective resistance of the two 100 kΩ resistors in parallel is $(100 \times 100)/(100 + 100) = 50$ kΩ. Therefore,
$V_{50\,k} = 12 \times 50/(10 + 50 + 33) = 6.45$ V.   *(Ans.)*

Current division

Figure 1.8 shows a current I flowing into a circuit that consists of two resistors R_1 and R_2 connected in parallel. The effective resistance of the circuit is $R_p = R_1 R_2/(R_1 + R_2)$ and so the voltage V dropped across the circuit is $V = IR_p = IR_1 R_2/(R_1 + R_2)$. The current I_1 that flows in resistor R_1 is $I_1 = V/R_1$ or

$$I_1 = IR_2/(R_1 + R_2) \tag{1.8}$$

Similarly, the current in R_2 is $I_2 = V/R_2$ or

$$I_2 = IR_1/(R_1 + R_2) \tag{1.9}$$

Thus the current division rule is: to determine the current flowing in either of two resistors connected in parallel when the total current

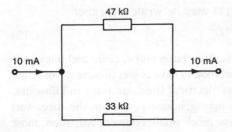

Fig. 1.9

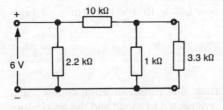

Fig. 1.10

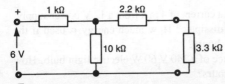

Fig. 1.11

is known divide the total current by the sum of the resistances and multiply by the resistance of the other resistor.

Example 1.7

For the circuit given in Fig. 1.9 calculate the current flowing in the 47 kΩ resistor.

Solution
From equation (1.8),
$$I_{47k} = 10 \times 33/(33 + 47) = 4.13 \text{ mA}. \quad (Ans.)$$

Example 1.8

Calculate the current flowing in the 3.3 kΩ resistor in the circuit of Fig. 1.10.

Solution
The total resistance connected across the 6 V supply voltage is $1 + 10(2.2 + 3.3)/(10 + 2.2 + 3.3) = 4.55$ kΩ. The current taken from the supply is $6/(4.55 \times 10^3) = 1.32$ mA. Therefore, the current in the 3.3 kΩ resistor is $I_{3.3k} = (1.32 \times 10)/(10 + 5.5) = 852 \ \mu\text{A}. \quad (Ans.)$

Example 1.9

Calculate the current flowing in the 3.3 kΩ resistor in the circuit of Fig. 1.11.

Solution
The resistance to the right of the 2.2 kΩ resistor $= 10 + 3.3/4.3 = 10.767$ kΩ. Total resistance $= (2.2 \times 10.767)/(2.2 + 10.767) = 1.827$ kΩ. Input current $= 6/1.827 = 3.284$ mA. Current in 10 kΩ resistor $= (3.284 \times 2.2)/(2.2 + 10.767) = 0.557$ mA. Therefore,
$$\text{current in 3.3 kΩ resistor} = 0.557/4.3 = 0.13 \text{ mA}. \quad (Ans.)$$

Electrical energy and power

Electrical energy is the capacity to do work and it is measured in joules. This unit is not of convenient size when large quantities of electrical energy are involved and in such cases the watt-hour and the kilowatt-hour are often used. One watt-hour is 3600 J and 1 kW hr = 3.6 MJ. If a voltage source of V volts supplies a current of I amperes for a time of t seconds to a purely resistive load, the energy W supplied to the load in that time is equal to

$$W = VIt \quad \text{J} \tag{1.10}$$

Electrical power is the rate of doing work and it is measured in joules/second or watts. Since the energy supplied in t seconds is VIt J, when $t = 1$ second the energy is VI joules. Hence,

$$P = VI \quad \text{W} \tag{1.11}$$

Since $V = IR$ equation (1.11) may be written as either

$$P = I^2 R \quad \text{or} \quad P = V^2/R \qquad (1.12)$$

Many electrical devices, such as lamp bulbs, radio and television receivers, and small electrical motors have power dissipation of a few watts; other devices, such as electrical fires, are rated in kilowatts. Large electrical generators may generate powers in the megawatt range. Electronic devices have much smaller power dissipation, most often only a few milliwatts and sometimes just some microwatts.

Example 1.10

(a) A transistor amplifier takes a current of 4 mA from a 12 V power supply. What power does the amplifier dissipate? How much energy is used if the amplifier is switched on for 12 hours?

(b) Calculate the 'hot' resistance of a 240 V 60 W electric light bulb. How much energy does it use in 3 hours?

Solution

(a) $P = 12 \times 4 \times 10^{-3} = 48$ mW. (*Ans.*)

$W = 48 \times 10^{-3} \times 60 \times 60 \times 12 = 2073.6$ J. (*Ans.*)

(b) $60 = 240^2/R$, $R = 960\Omega$. (*Ans.*)

$W = 60 \times 60 \times 60 \times 3 = 648 \times 10^3$ J $= 180$ W hr. (*Ans.*)

Maximum power transfer

Many instances occur in electronic and communication engineering where a voltage source is to be connected to a load and the maximum power is to be transferred from the source to the load. Fig. 1.12(a)

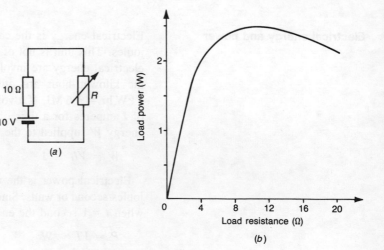

Fig. 1.12 Maximum power transfer

Table 1.2

R	0	2	4	6	8	10	12	14	16	18
I	1	0.833	0.714	0.625	0.556	0.5	0.455	0.41	0.385	0.357
P	0	1.389	2.041	2.344	2.469	2.5	2.479	2.431	2.367	2.296

shows a voltage source of 10 V and internal resistance 10 Ω connected to a variable resistance R. The current flowing in the circuit is $I = 10/(10 + R)$ and the power dissipated in the load is $P = I^2R = [10/(10 + R)]^2$. If the value of R is increased in a number of steps starting from 0 Ω it is found that the power dissipated in R increases at first and thereafter it decreases. Suppose that R is increased in 2 Ω steps from 0 to 16 Ω. The values then obtained for both the current I in the circuit and the power P dissipated in the load R are given in Table 1.2 and are shown plotted in Fig. 1.12(b).

It is clear that the maximum power is dissipated in the load when the load resistance is equal to the source resistance.

Example 1.11

A voltage source of e.m.f. 2 V and internal resistance 50 Ω is connected to a resistive load. Determine (a) the resistance of the load for maximum power to be dissipated in it, and (b) the value of this maximum power.

Solution

(a) For maximum power transfer $R_L = 50\,\Omega$.   (*Ans.*)
(b) $I = 2/100 = 0.02$ A and the power dissipated in the load is
$P = 0.02^2 \times 50 = 20$ mW.   (*Ans.*)

Kirchhoff's laws

When two, or more, voltages are simultaneously applied to a circuit the calculation of the currents, etc., in the circuit becomes a little more difficult. Two laws, due to Kirchhoff, or their derivatives, can be employed to carry out the calculations. The first of Kirchhoff's laws is commonly known as the *current law* and the second is known as the *voltage law*.

The current law states 'At any junction, or *node*, in a network the algebraic sum of the currents flowing into the junction is equal to the algebraic sum of the currents flowing away from the junction.' Consider, for example, the network shown in Fig. 1.13 and use the law to find the unknown currents in the circuit. Then,

$I_1 = 1 + 1.4 = 2.4$ mA, $I_2 = 4 - 2.4 = 1.6$ mA,
$I_3 = I_2 + 2 = 1.6 + 2 = 3.6$ mA, $I_4 = 3 - 1.4 = 1.6$ mA,
$I_5 = 3.6 - 1.6 = 2$ mA.

The voltage law states 'The algebraic sum of the e.m.f.s acting around any closed loop in a network is equal to the algebraic sum

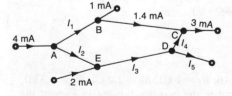

Fig. 1.13 Illustrating Kirchhoff's current law

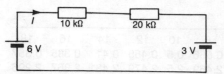

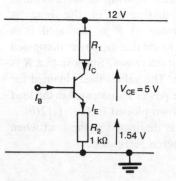

Fig. 1.14 Illustrating Kirchhoff's voltage law

Fig. 1.15

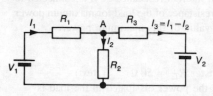

Fig. 1.16 Kirchhoff's law

of the voltage drops across the resistances in that loop.' Referring to Fig. 1.14, $6 - 3 = I(10 + 20) \times 10^3$, or $I = 3/(30 \times 10^3) = 100\,\mu\text{A}$.

Example 1.12

Figure 1.15 shows a part of a transistor amplifier. The base current I_B is very small so that the collector current I_C may be taken as being equal to the emitter current I_E. Calculate (a) the collector current I_C, (b) the collector resistor R_1, and (c) the power dissipated in (i) the transistor, (ii) in both R_1 and R_2, and (iii) the circuit as a whole.

Solution

(a) $I_C = I_E = 1.54/1000 = 1.54\,\text{mA}$.   (*Ans.*)
(b) From the voltage law, $12 - 5 - 1.54 = 1.54 \times 10^{-3}R_1$
$R_1 = 5.46/(1.54 \times 10^{-3}) = 3545$
$= 3.6\,\text{k}\Omega$ preferred value.   (*Ans.*)
(c) Power dissipated in transistor $= 1.54 \times 10^{-3} \times 5$
$= 7.7\,\text{mW}$.   (*Ans.*)
in $R_1 = 1.54 \times 10^{-3} \times 5.46 = 8.4\,\text{mW}$.   (*Ans.*)
in $R_2 = 1.54 \times 10^{-3} \times 1.54 = 2.37\,\text{mW}$.   (*Ans.*)
in complete circuit $= 7.7 + 8.4 + 2.37 = 18.47\,\text{mW}$
or $12 \times 1.54 \times 10^{-3} = 18.48\,\text{mW}$.   (*Ans.*)

To analyse a T network such as that shown in Fig. 1.16 first apply Kirchhoff's current law to label the currents in the various resistors and then use the voltage law to set up equations from which the network can be solved. The number of equations required is equal to the number of unknown currents to be determined. The current leaving the voltage source V_1 can be labelled I_1 and this current flows through resistor R_1 to the junction, or *node*, A. Here the current will divide into two parts, one part flowing via R_2 and the other part via R_3. If the current that flows down through resistor R_2 is labelled as I_2 the current flowing through resistor R_3 and voltage source V_2 can be labelled as I_3. It will not be known at this point in which direction I_3 will flow; this will depend upon the relative values of the two voltage sources and of the three resistors. Assume for the moment that I_3 flows through R_3 from left to right then $I_3 = I_1 - I_2$, as shown in Fig. 1.16. If any of the assumed directions for the three currents is incorrect then the calculated value for that current will come out as a negative value. Since there are two unknown currents, i.e., I_1 and I_2, two equations are necessary.

Example 1.13

In the network shown in Fig. 1.16, $R_1 = 1\,\text{k}\Omega$, $R_2 = 2.2\,\text{k}\Omega$, $R_3 = 3.3\,\text{k}\Omega$, $V_1 = 6\,\text{V}$ and $V_2 = 1.5\,\text{V}$. Calculate the currents flowing in each of the resistors.

Solution
Applying Kirchhoff's voltage law to (*a*) loop $V_1R_1R_2$ and working in
kilohms, $6 = 1\,I_1 + 2.2\,I_2 = I_1 + 2.2\,I_2$ (1.13)
and (*b*) to loop $R_2R_3V_2$, $-1.5 = -2.2\,I_2 + 3.3(I_1 - I_2)$
$$= 3.3\,I_1 - 5.5\,I_2 \tag{1.14}$$
Multiply equation (1.13) by 3.3 to give
$$19.8 = 3.3\,I_1 + 7.26\,I_2 \tag{1.15}$$
Subtracting equation (1.14) from (1.15) gives,
$21.3 = 12.76\,I_2$ or $I_2 = 1.67\,\text{mA}$. (*Ans.*)
Substituting this value of I_2 into equation (1.13), $6 = I_1 + 2.2 \times 1.67$
or $I_1 = 2.33\,\text{mA}$. (*Ans.*)
Therefore, $I_3 = 2.33 - 1.67 = 0.66\,\text{mA}$. (*Ans.*)

If any of the calculated currents had been negative it would mean
that that current actually flowed in the opposite direction to that
assumed. Suppose, for example, that the 1.5 V source in Fig. 1.16
is replaced by a 4.5 V source. Then equation (1.14) would become
$-4.5 = 3.3\,I_1 - 5.5\,I_2$ and subtracting (1.14) from (1.15) gives
$24.3 = 12.76\,I_2$ or $I_2 = 1.9\,\text{mA}$. Now $I_1 = 6 - 2.2 \times 1.9 =$
$1.82\,\text{mA}$ and hence $I_3 = 1.82 - 1.9 = -0.08\,\text{mA}$. This means that
now the current in the 3.3 kΩ resistor flows from right to left.

There are two variations of the basic Kirchhoff's laws that can often
reduce the amount of work involved in the solution of a network.
These two alternatives are known as the circulating currents method
and nodal analysis.

Circulating currents

The need to employ Kirchhoff's current law to decide the direction
of the currents flowing in the various loops of a network can be
avoided by the use of *circulating currents*. Each loop in a network
is assumed to have a current that flows around it in the same direction,
either clockwise or anticlockwise, as the currents in all the other loops
in the network. An example of this is shown by Fig. 1.18 which
contains two loops each of which has a current that is assumed to
flow in the clockwise direction. If any current actually flows in the
opposite direction to that assumed the calculation of that current will
give a negative result. The current in resistor R_2 is the difference
between the currents I_1 and I_2.

Nodal analysis

Nodal analysis makes use of Kirchhoff's current law. The currents
entering, and leaving, each junction, or *node*, in the network are
summed to zero to obtain the equations that describe the network.
For the network shown in Fig. 1.18 the equation is:

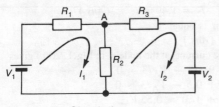

Fig. 1.17 Circulating currents

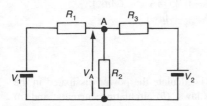

Fig. 1.18 Nodal analysis

$$(V_1 - V_A)/R_1 - V_A/R_2 - (V_A - V_2)/R_3 = 0 \qquad (1.16)$$

Usually nodal analysis will give the least number of equations to be solved.

Example 1.14

Calculate the currents flowing in each resistor in Fig. 1.19 using (*a*) Kirchhoff's laws, (*b*) circulating currents, and (*c*) nodal analysis.

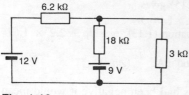

Fig. 1.19

Solution

Working in kilohms throughout,

(*a*) Kirchhoff's laws: For the left-hand loop in Fig. 1.20(*a*)

$$12 - 9 = 6.2 I_1 + 18 I_2 \qquad (1.17)$$

For the right-hand loop, $9 = -18 I_2 + 3(I_1 - I_2)$

$$9 = 3 I_1 - 21 I_2 \qquad (1.18)$$

Dividing equation (1.17) by 6 and (1.18) by 7 gives

$$0.5 = 1.03 I_1 + 3 I_2 \qquad (1.19)$$
$$1.29 = 0.43 I_1 - 3 I_2 \qquad (1.20)$$

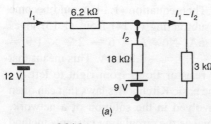

(*a*)

Adding (1.19) and (1.20), $1.79 = 1.46 I_1$ or $I_1 = 1.22\,\text{mA}$. (*Ans.*)

Substitute the value of I_1 into equation (1.17) to get

$$3 = 6.2 \times 1.22 + 18 I_2 \quad \text{or} \quad I_2 = -0.25\,\text{mA}. \quad (Ans.)$$

Lastly, $I_3 = 1.22 - (-0.25) = 1.47\,\text{mA}$. (*Ans.*)

(*b*) Circulating currents: For the left-hand loop in Fig. 1.20(*b*)

$$12 - 9 = 6.2 I_1 + 18 I_1 - 18 I_2$$
$$3 = 24.2 I_1 - 18 I_2 \qquad (1.21)$$

For the right-hand loop, $9 = 21 I_2 - 18 I_1$ \qquad (1.22)

Divide equation (1.21) by 6 and (1.22) by 7 to obtain

$$0.5 = 4.03 I_1 - 3 I_2 \qquad (1.23)$$
$$1.29 = -2.57 I_1 + 3 I_2 \qquad (1.24)$$

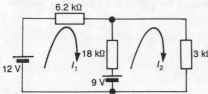

(*b*)

Add equations (1.23) and (1.24) together to get $1.79 = 1.46 I_1$

or $I_1 = 1.23\,\text{mA}$. (*Ans.*)

Substitute this value into equation (1.21),

$$3 = 24.2 \times 1.23 - 18 I_2, \quad \text{or} \quad I_2 = 1.49\,\text{mA}. \quad (Ans.)$$

The current in the 18 kΩ resistor is equal to

$$I_1 - I_2 = -0.26\,\text{mA}. \quad (Ans.)$$

(*c*) Nodal analysis: summing the currents at the node A in Fig.1. 20(*c*) gives

$$(12 - V_A)/6.2 - (V_A - 9)/18 - V_A/3 = 0$$
$$1.94 - V_A/6.2 - V_A/18 + 0.5 - V_A/3 = 0$$
$$2.44 = V_A (1/6.2 + 1/18 + 1/3) = 0.55 V_A,$$

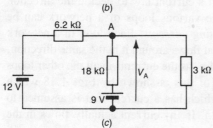

(*c*)

Fig. 1.20

or $V_A = 2.44/0.55 = 4.44\,\text{V}$.

Therefore, $I_1 = (12 - 4.44)/6.2 = 1.22\,\text{mA}$. (*Ans.*)

$$I_2 = (4.44 - 9)/18 = -0.25\,\text{mA}. \quad (Ans.)$$

and $\qquad I_3 = 4.44/3 = 1.48\,\text{mA}$. (*Ans.*)

Example 1.15

For the network shown in Fig. 1.21 calculate the power dissipated in the 10 kΩ resistor using (*a*) Kirchhoff's laws, (*b*) circulating currents, and (*c*) nodal analysis.

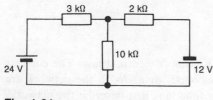

Fig. 1.21

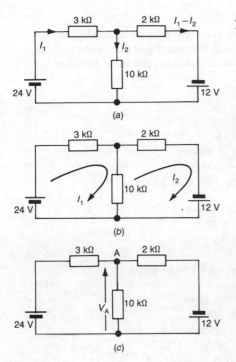

Fig. 1.22

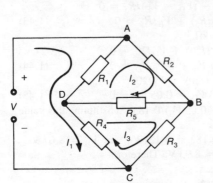

Fig. 1.23 Bridge network

Solution
Working in kilohms,
(a) Kirchhoff's laws: From the left-hand loop in Fig. 1.22(a),
$$24 = 3I_1 + 10I_2 \tag{1.25}$$
From the right-hand loop,
$$-12 = -10I_2 + 2(I_1 - I_2)$$
$$-12 = 2I_1 - 12I_2 \tag{1.26}$$
Multiply equation (1.26) by 1.5 to give
$$-18 = 3I_1 - 18I_2 \tag{1.27}$$
Subtract equation (1.27) from equation (1.25) to give
$$42 = 28I_2, \quad \text{or} \quad I_2 = 1.5\,\text{mA}.$$
Therefore the power dissipated in the 10 kΩ resistor is
$$P = (1.5 \times 10^{-3})^2 \times 10^3 = 22.5\,\text{mW}. \quad (Ans.)$$
(b) Circulating currents: From the left-hand loop of Fig.1. 22(b),
$$24 = 13I_1 - 10I_2 \tag{1.28}$$
From the right-hand loop,
$$-12 = -10I_1 + 12I_2 \tag{1.29}$$
Multiply equation (1.28) by 1.2 to give
$$28.8 = 15.6I_1 - 12I_2 \tag{1.30}$$
Adding (1.29) and (1.30) gives $16.8 = 5.6I_1$, or $I_1 = 3\,\text{mA}$.
Substitute in equation (1.28) to get
$$24 = 39 - 10I_2 \text{ or } I_2 = -1.5\,\text{mA}.$$
The current in the 10 kΩ resistor is $I_1 - I_2 = 1.5\,\text{mA}$.
Therefore, power dissipated in the 10 kΩ resistor = 22.5 mW. (Ans.)
(c) Nodal analysis: From Fig. 1.22(c),
$$(24 - V_A)/3 - V_A/10 - (V_A - 12)/2 = 0$$
$$8 - V_A/3 - V_A/10 - V_A/2 + 6 = 0$$
$$14 = V_A(1/3 + 1/10 + 1/2) = 0.93V_A, \quad \text{or} \quad V_A = 15\,\text{V}.$$
Therefore the current in the 10 kΩ resistor is 1.5 mA and the power dissipated is 22.5 mW. (Ans.)

Bridge networks

There are a number of *bridge* networks in which the resistors are connected neither in series nor in parallel and Fig. 1.23 shows the network that is the basis of the *Wheatstone Bridge*. For such a network it is easiest to employ the circulating current method of solution and the network equations are given by equations (1.31) to (1.33).

Loop ADC, $V = I_1(R_1 + R_2) - I_2R_1 - I_3R_4$ (1.31)
Loop ABD, $0 = I_2(R_1 + R_2 + R_5) - I_1R_1 - I_3R_5$ (1.32)
Loop BCD, $0 = I_3(R_3 + R_4 + R_5) - I_1R_4 - I_2R_5$ (1.33)

Example 1.16

If, in Fig. 1.23, $R_1 = 10\,\text{k}\Omega$, $R_2 = 20\,\text{k}\Omega$, $R_3 = 47\,\text{k}\Omega$, $R_4 = 30\,\text{k}\Omega$, and $R_5 = 20\,\text{k}\Omega$, calculate the power dissipated in the network when a 12 V power supply is connected across the points A and C.

Solution

Three simultaneous equations are necessary since there are three unknown currents. The method of solution is to eliminate one of the unknown currents, say I_3, to obtain just two equations and then to solve these equations for I_1 and I_2.

From equations (1.31) to (1.33),

$$12 = 40 I_1 - 10 I_2 - 30 I_3 \tag{1.34}$$

$$0 = -10 I_1 + 50 I_2 - 20 I_3 \tag{1.35}$$

$$0 = -30 I_1 - 20 I_2 + 97 I_3 \tag{1.36}$$

Multiply equation (1.34) by 2/3 to obtain

$$8 = 26.67 I_1 - 6.67 I_2 - 20 I_3 \tag{1.37}$$

Subtract equation (1.35) from equation (1.37) to give

$$8 = 36.67 I_1 - 56.67 I_2 \tag{1.38}$$

Multiply equation (1.36) by 20/97 to get

$$0 = -6.19 I_1 - 4.12 I_2 + 20 I_3 \tag{1.39}$$

Adding equations (1.35) and (1.39) gives

$$0 = -16.19 I_1 + 45.88 I_2 \tag{1.40}$$

Now multiply equation (1.38) by 16.19/36.67 to get

$$3.53 = 16.19 I_1 - 25.02 I_2 \tag{1.41}$$

Adding equations (1.40) and (1.41) gives

$$3.53 = 20.68 I_2, \quad \text{or} \quad I_2 = 169 \, \mu A.$$

Substituting this value of I_2 into equation (1.40) gives,

$$16.19 I_1 = 45.88 \times 169, \quad \text{or} \quad I_1 = 479 \, \mu A.$$

Then substituting for both I_1 and I_2 in equation (1.35) gives

$$20 I_3 = -4790 + 50 \times 169, \quad \text{or} \quad I_3 = 183 \, \mu A.$$

Therefore, current in $R_1 = I_1 - I_2 = 479 - 169 = 310 \, \mu A$,

  power dissipated $= (310 \times 10^{-6})^2 \times 10 \times 10^3 = 961 \, \mu W$,

  current in $R_2 = I_2 = 169 \, \mu A$ and   power $= 571 \, \mu W$,

  current in $R_3 = I_3 = 183 \, \mu A$ and   power $= 1.574 \, mW$,

  current in $R_4 = I_1 - I_3 = 296 \, \mu A$ and   power $= 2.628 \, mW$,

  current in $R_5 = I_2 - I_3 = -14 \, \mu A$ and   power $= 3.9 \, \mu W$.

The total power dissipated in the bridge network is the sum of the individual powers, i.e., $P = 5.74 \, mW$.   (*Ans.*)

Alternatively, using nodal analysis:

Node B: $(V - V_B)/R_2 - V_B/R_3 - (V_B - V_D)/R_5 = 0$

$$V/R_2 - V_B/(1/R_2 + 1/R_3 + 1/R_5) + V_D/R_5 = 0 \tag{1.42}$$

Node D: $(V - V_D)/R_1 - V_D/R_4 - (V_D - V_B)/R_5 = 0$

$$V/R_1 - V_D(1/R_1 + 1/R_4 + 1/R_5) + V_B/R_5 = 0 \tag{1.43}$$

Substituting values and working in kΩ,

$$12/20 - V_B(1/20 + 1/47 + 1/20) + V_D/20 = 0$$

$$0.6 - 0.121 V_B + 0.05 V_D = 0 \tag{1.44}$$

and $12/10 - V_D(1/10 + 1/30 + 1/20) + V_B/20 =$

$$1.2 - 0.183 V_D + 0.05 V_B = 0 \tag{1.45}$$

From equation (1.45), $V_D = (1.2 + 0.05 V_B)/0.183$. Substituting this value into equation (1.44) gives

$$0.6 + 0.05(1.2 + 0.05 V_B)/0.183 = 0.121 V_B, \quad \text{or} \quad V_B = 8.67 \, V.$$

Hence, from equation (1.44), $V_D = 8.93 \, V$. Therefore,

$$I_1 = (12 - 8.93)/10 = 307 \, \mu A.$$

$$I_2 = (12 - 8.67)/20 = 176 \, \mu A.$$

$$I_3 = 8.67/47 = 185 \, \mu A.$$

$$I_4 = 8.93/30 = 298 \, \mu A.$$

and $I_5 = (8.93 - 8.67)/20 = 13 \, \mu A.$

The small differences in the calculated values obtained using the two methods are caused by the rounding-off of figures at intermediate points in the calculations. The errors thus caused are, however, smaller than those due to the tolerances of the resistors.

2 Electric fields and capacitance

An electric field is the region in the vicinity of an electric charge in which a force will be exerted upon any other electric charge. This force will either be one of attraction or of repulsion depending upon whether or not the two charges are of the same, or of opposite, polarity. Charges having the same polarity repel one another while charges of opposite polarity attract. The direction of the electric field indicates the direction in which the force will be exerted upon a positive charge and some examples are given by Fig. 2.1. Each electric field is represented by lines of *electric flux*. The electric flux is the quantity of charge that is moved from one conductor to the other and it is directly proportional to the charge that has created it. Electric flux is measured in coulombs. Unit flux leaves a positive charge of one coulomb and enters a negative charge of one coulomb. This means that the magnitudes of the flux Ψ and the charge Q are equal to one another, i.e., $\Psi = Q$ in coulombs. All flux lines enter or leave a conductor at right-angles to the conductor, this means that for a conductor of circular cross-section the flux lines either enter or leave radially.

Figure 2.1(a) shows an isolated positive charge; the lines of electric flux leave the charge radially and follow straight-line paths. The electric field is reversed for an isolated negative charge as Fig. 2.1(b) shows, and now the lines of electric flux enter the charge radially. When two charges are placed in the vicinity of one another the electric field produced by each of the charges will be affected by the electric

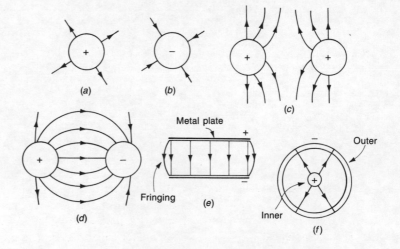

Fig. 2.1 Electric fields; (a) of isolated positive charge, (b) of isolated negative charge, (c) of two like charges, (d) of two unlike charges, (e) between two parallel metal plates, and (f) in a coaxial conductor

field of the other charge. Figure 2.1(*c*) shows the case when the two charges are both of the same polarity; since both charges are positive the flux lines leave the charges radially (as in Fig. 2.1(*a*)). The lines of flux are mutually repellent, and are unable to intersect one another and so the combined electric field which is set up has the general shape shown. When the two adjacent charges are of opposite polarity the flux lines move from the positively charged conductor to the negatively charged conductor to give the electric field pattern shown by Fig. 2.1(*d*). Figures 2.1(*c*) and (*d*) are the electric field patterns for a pair of conductors carrying currents in (*a*) the same direction and (*b*) in opposite directions. Figure 2.1(*e*) shows the electric field pattern that will exist between two parallel metal plates; in the space between the plates the flux lines go directly from the positive plate to the negative plate. At the two ends of the plates some *fringing* occurs. Lastly, Fig. 2.1(*f*) shows the electric field pattern in a coaxial conductor assuming that the inner conductor is positively charged and the outer conductor is negatively charged.

Since unlike charges attract one another the force exerted between two charged conductors of opposite polarity is one of attraction. The two conductors must be kept apart and so the intervening space must be filled with some kind of insulating material, or *dielectric*. Some suitable dielectrics are listed in Table 2.1; one possible dielectric is air, if this is used then the use of some kind of insulating spacers will obviously be necessary.

Electric potential

The potential of a point in an electric field is a measure of the amount of work in joules that a charge of one coulomb situated at that point is capable of doing. The potential is equal to the work done by the charge in moving to that point from a point of zero potential, i.e., 0 V. Electric potential may be either positive or negative. Potential is measured in joules/coulomb or volts. The *potential difference* (p.d.) between two points in an electric field is the difference between the electric potentials of the two points.

When an electric charge Q is caused to move by an applied voltage the moving charge receives a certain amount of energy because some work must be done by the charge. One joule of work is done when a charge of one coulomb is moved between two points that have a potential difference of one volt between them. Therefore, W joules of work is done if Q coulombs are moved through a p.d. of V volts.

$$\text{Voltage} = \text{energy/charge} = W/Q \quad \text{V} \tag{2.1}$$

This relationship can be arrived at in another manner; energy $W = \text{power } P \text{ times time } t = VIt = VQt/t = VQ \text{ or } V = W/Q$.

When a charge of one coulomb is moved between two parallel metal plates the work done is numerically equal to the p.d. across the plates. Figure 2.2 shows two points A and B in the electric field between two parallel metal plates. The p.d. across the plates is V volts. To

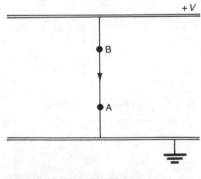

Fig. 2.2 Electric potential

move a positive charge of one coulomb from the point A to the point B against the field requires work to be *done on* the charge, but if the same charge is moved from point B to point A in the same direction as the field work is *done by* the charge. This means that when the charge is at point B it has a higher electric potential, i.e., a capacity to do work, than when the charge is at the point A.

Example 2.1

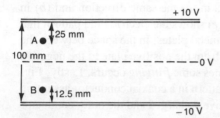

Fig. 2.3

Figure 2.3 shows two parallel metal plates that are 100 mm apart and that have +10 V applied to the top plate and −10 V applied to the bottom plate. Calculate the work done by, or done on, a positive charge of 2 coulombs situated at (*a*) point A, (*b*) point B, when the charge is moved to the point midway between the two plates. What is the p.d. between (*c*) the two plates, and (*d*) between the points A and B?

Solution

(*a*) The midway point is at 0 V and the point A is at +5 V. When the charge moves in the direction of the electric field from +5 V to 0 V it will do work of $2 \times 5 = 10$ J.   (*Ans.*)

(*b*) Point B is at −7.5 V. Moving the charge against the direction of the electric field from −7.5 V to 0 V requires $2 \times 7.5 = 15$ J work to be done on the charge.   (*Ans.*)

Referring to Fig. 2.3, the p.d. between the two plates is 20 V, and between points A and B is $5 - (-7.5) = 12.5$ V.   (*Ans.*)

Electric flux density

The electric flux density D of an electric field is the electric flux per metre squared of area, i.e.,

$$D = \Psi/A = Q/A \ \text{C/m}^2 \tag{2.2}$$

where Q is the charge in coulombs and A is the area in m^2 over which the flux is distributed.

Example 2.2

Calculate the charge on two parallel 10^4 mm^2 metal plates if the flux density between the plates is 40 mC/m^2.

Solution
From equation (2.2),
$$Q = AD = 10^4 \times 10^{-6} \times 40 \times 10^{-3} = 400 \ \mu\text{C}. \quad (Ans.)$$

Electric field strength

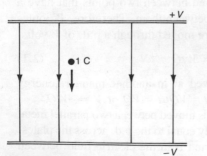

Fig. 2.4 Electric field strength

When a positive charge of 1 coulomb is placed in the electric field between two parallel metal plates, as in Fig. 2.4, it will be subjected to two forces. There will be a repulsive force exerted by the positively charged upper plate on the charge, and an attractive force exerted by the negatively charged lower plate. The resultant force will move the charge downwards towards the lower plate. The magnitude of the total force exerted upon the charge is known as the *electric field strength E* in newtons/coulomb.

The force exerted upon a charge of Q coulombs will be Q times as large as the force exerted upon 1 coulomb and hence

$$F = QE \quad N \quad (Ans.)$$

Example 2.3

Calculate the force exerted on an electron in a uniform electric field whose electric field strength is 40×10^6 N/C.

Solution
The charge on an electron $= 1.602 \times 10^{-19}$ C. Therefore,
force exerted $= 1.602 \times 10^{-19} \times 40 \times 10^6 = 6.41 \times 10^{-12}$ N. (*Ans.*)

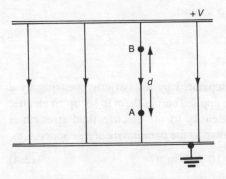

Fig. 2.5 Potential gradient

The electric field strength is more commonly expressed in terms of the p.d. between the metal plates and the separation of the plates. Figure 2.5 shows two points A and B that are d metres apart in the uniform electric field between two parallel metal plates. The electric potentials at the two points are V_A and V_B respectively. If a charge of 1 C is moved from point A to point B by the electric force exerted upon the charge the work done will be Ed, and therefore, $E = (V_B - V_A)/d$.

$(V_A - V_B)/d$ is the *potential gradient* between points A and B but since the electric force is in the opposite direction to the potential gradient $E = -$potential gradient. The p.d. across the metal plates is V volts and so

$$E = V/d \quad V/m \tag{2.3}$$

Example 2.4

The voltage applied across two parallel metal plates 0.1 mm apart is 10 V. Calculate the electric field strength between the plates.

Solution
From equation (2.3), $E = 10/(0.1 \times 10^{-3}) = 100$ kV/m. (*Ans.*)

Example 2.5

The insulated gate terminal of a mosfet is 100 nm thick. Calculate the electric field strength in the gate region when the voltage across it is 2 V.

Solution
$$E = 2/(100 \times 10^{-9}) = 20 \text{ MV/m.} \quad (Ans.)$$

Table 2.1 Relative permittivities of common dielectrics

Air	1.0006	Paper	2–4
Aluminium oxide	7	Polycarbonate	2.8
Bakelite	4–8	Polyethylene	2.3
		Polypropylene	2.5
Ceramic	10–100	Polystyrene	2.5
Glass	4–10	Rubber	2
Mica	2.5–8	Tantalum oxide	10–28
Mylar	3	Teflon	2
Oil	2.5	Water	80

Clearly this is a very large value and more than enough to break down the gate semiconductor material. Once breakdown has occurred the gate will not be insulated from the channel and the mosfet will no longer work. The charge necessary to cause breakdown is not large and this means that a voltage high enough to destroy the mosfet can easily be produced by merely touching the gate terminal with a finger or with a tool. Great care is therefore required when handling mosfets and when fitting them into a circuit.

Permittivity

When two conductors are separated by air (strictly speaking by a vacuum), and have a voltage applied across them to set up an electric field the ratio of the flux density to the electric field strength is constant. This constant is known as the *permittivity of free space*, i.e.,

$$\epsilon_0 = D/E = 8.854 \times 10^{-12} \, \text{F/m} \tag{2.4}$$

When a dielectric is placed in the space between the two conductors without altering the voltage applied across the plates the flux density is increased but the electric field strength remains unchanged. This means that the permittivity of the system must have increased and now

$$D/E = \epsilon_0 \epsilon_r \tag{2.5}$$

where ϵ_r is the *relative permittivity* of the dielectric. The product $\epsilon_0 \epsilon_r$ is known as the *absolute permittivity* of the dielectric material.

Some typical figures for the relative permittivity of some commonly employed dielectric materials are given by Table 2.1.

Capacitance

Capacitance is the property possessed by two adjacent conductors that are separated from one another by an insulating material, or dielectric, that allows the dielectric to store an electrical charge. The unit of capacitance is the farad (F) but for all practical purposes this unit is far too large. Consequently, sub-multiples of the farad, such as the micro-farad ($\mu\text{F} = 10^{-6} \, \text{F}$), the nano-farad ($\text{nF} = 10^{-9} \, \text{F}$), and the pico-farad ($\text{pF} = 10^{-12} \, \text{F}$), are always employed.

A capacitance is equal to 1 F if a charge of 1 C causes the potential difference between two conductors to change by 1 V. If a charge of Q coulombs changes the p.d. by V volts then the charge that will give 1 V change in the p.d. is equal to Q/V. Therefore,

$$C = Q/V \quad \text{F} \tag{2.6}$$

Example 2.6

A charge of 10 μC changes the p.d. between two conductors by 1 V. Calculate the capacitance of the conductors.

Solution
From equation (2.6), C = $(10 \times 10^{-6})/1 = 10\,\mu$F.   (*Ans.*)

The parallel-plate capacitor

A *capacitor* is an electrical component that possesses a particular value of capacitance. Many different types of capacitor exist but the simplest is the parallel-plate capacitor that consists of two metal plates or electrodes. The two plates each have an area of A m^2 and they are separated by a dielectric d m thick of relative permittivity ϵ_r.

When the capacitor has been charged to have a charge of Q coulombs on, and a voltage V across, its electrodes $\epsilon = D/E = Qd/AV$, or

$$Q/V = C = \epsilon_0\epsilon_r\, A/d \quad \text{F} \tag{2.7}$$

Thus, the capacitance of a parallel-plate capacitor is directly proportional to both the area of its plates and the relative permittivity of its dielectric, and inversely proportional to the thickness of the dielectric.

Example 2.7

Calculate the charge stored by a parallel-plate capacitor whose 0.01 m^2 plates are 0.1 mm apart, if the capacitor voltage is 12 V. $\epsilon_r = 3$.

Solution
$E = V/d = 12/(0.1 \times 10^{-3}) = 120 \times 10^3$ V/m.
$D = \epsilon_0\epsilon_r E = 8.854 \times 10^{-12} \times 3 \times 120 \times 10^3 = 3.19\,\mu$C/m^2.
$Q = DA = 3.19 \times 10^{-6} \times 0.01 = 31.9$ nC.   (*Ans.*)
Alternatively, $C = \epsilon_0\epsilon_r A/d = (8.854 \times 10^{-12} \times 3 \times 0.01)/(0.1 \times 10^{-3}) = 2.66$ nF. $Q = CV = 2.66 \times 10^{-9} \times 12 = 31.9$ nC.   (*Ans.*)

Charging a capacitor

A capacitor may be charged to store a charge Q when it has a voltage V across its terminals, the relationship between the two quantities being

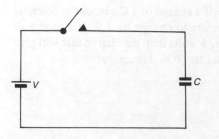

Fig. 2.6 Charging a capacitor

given by $Q = VC$. A capacitor is charged by causing a charge to flow into it. Suppose that a capacitor is charged by connecting it to a battery as shown by Fig. 2.6. When the switch is closed electrons at the upper plate of the capacitor are attracted by the positive terminal of the battery and there is a movement of electrons from the upper plate to the battery. This is, of course, equivalent to a flow of current from the positive terminal of the battery to the upper plate of the capacitor. At the same time, electrons are moved from the negative terminal of the battery to the lower plate of the capacitor and this is equivalent to a flow of current from the lower plate to the battery. Note that no current actually flows through the capacitor since its dielectric is an insulator. As a result the upper plate becomes deficient of electrons while the lower plate gains a surplus of electrons. This means that the upper plate becomes positively charged and the lower plate becomes negatively charged. The two charges are of equal magnitude and the voltage across the capacitor terminals is equal to the battery voltage.

The charging of a capacitor may be achieved using either a constant current source or a constant voltage source. A constant current source has a very high output resistance (which may be obtained by continuously varying its voltage to keep the supplied current at a constant value) and it is able to deliver a constant value of current to a capacitor. A constant voltage source, such as a battery or a power supply unit, will deliver a charging current that falls as the voltage across the capacitor terminals increases.

Constant current charging

When a constant value I of current is used to charge a capacitor the charge on each capacitor electrode after the current has flowed for a time t seconds is $Q = It$ coulombs. The voltage across the terminals of the capacitor is then $V = Q/C = It/C$. Since the ratio I/C is a constant quantity the capacitor voltage will be directly proportional to the time for which the current has flowed. A plot of the capacitor voltage against time is a straight-line graph.

Example 2.8

A 2.2 μF capacitor is charged by a constant current of 22 μA. If the capacitor is initially discharged plot its voltage/time relationship. How long does it take for the capacitor voltage to reach 5 V?

Solution
$$V = It/C = (22 \times 10^{-6})t/(2.2 \times 10^{-6}) = 10\,t.$$
In 1 second the capacitor voltage will be 10 V, in 2 seconds it will be 20 V and so on. The voltage/time graph for the capacitor is given by Fig. 2.7. The time taken for the voltage to become equal to 5 V can be found from the graph, or from $5 = 10\,t$, $t = 0.5$ s.   (*Ans.*)

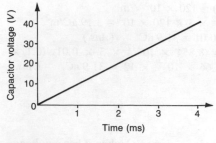

Fig. 2.7

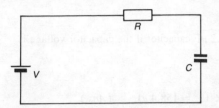

Fig. 2.8 Constant voltage charging of a capacitor

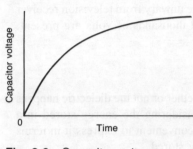

Fig. 2.9 Capacitor voltage

Constant voltage charging

When an initially uncharged capacitor is first connected to a constant voltage source via a resistor R as shown by Fig. 2.8 the initial current I_{in} that flows in the circuit is $I_{in} = V/R$ since the capacitor voltage is zero. This current partially charges the capacitor and so its voltage rises to v_C volts; then the voltage across R is reduced to $V - v_C$ and hence the current falls to $(V - v_C)/R$. The reduction in the current reduces the rate at which charge is supplied to the capacitor and this, in turn, reduces the rate of increase of the capacitor voltage. The more charge that is delivered to the capacitor the greater becomes the voltage across the capacitor's terminals and the smaller becomes the current $(V - v_C)/R$ flowing in the resistor. When, eventually, the capacitor voltage becomes equal to the applied voltage V there will be no current flowing in the circuit and the capacitor is then said to be fully charged. The increase in the capacitor voltage with time is *exponential* and it is shown by Fig. 2.9.

A charged capacitor will not retain its charge indefinitely once the source of charge has been removed. The dielectric does not have an infinitely high resistance and so there will always be a small leakage path through which some charges can move and cancel one another out. However, the charge can be retained for quite a long time by some capacitors and care should always be taken to ensure that a large-value capacitor has been fully discharged before its terminals are touched. Otherwise an electric shock might be experienced even though the power supplies have been switched off. A capacitor is discharged by connecting its terminals to a resistive path through which a discharge current can flow to remove the charge stored at its electrodes. Charged capacitors can represent a serious safety hazard to personnel even after the equipment has been switched off. EN 60 950 (formerly IEC 950) requires that bleed resistors are fitted to remove charge to all networks that have a total capacitance of $0.1\ \mu F$ or more.

Energy stored in a capacitor

Once a capacitor has been charged up and has a voltage V across its terminals energy will be stored in its dielectric. If the capacitor was charged with a constant current its terminal voltage will have risen linearly with time and so the average voltage will be $V/2$ volts. The energy supplied in t seconds is $VIt/2\ J$ and since zero energy is dissipated within the capacitor* this must also be the energy stored within the capacitor. Therefore

*This is not strictly true but (the small) losses in capacitors are beyond the scope of this book.

$$\text{energy stored } W = VIt/2 = VQ/2 = CV^2/2 \quad J \qquad (2.8)$$
$$\text{or} \qquad W = Q^2/2C \quad J \qquad (2.9)$$

Example 2.9

Calculate the energy stored in a 2.2 μF capacitor if the capacitor voltage is (*a*) 12 V, and (*b*) 120 V.

Solution

    (*a*) $W = 0.5 \times 2.2 \times 10^{-6} \times 12^2 = 158.4\ \mu J.$ (*Ans.*)
    (*b*) $W = 0.5 \times 2.2 \times 10^{-6} \times 120^2 = 15.84\ mJ.$ (*Ans.*)

Clearly the higher the voltage to which a capacitor has been charged the greater is the energy that is stored within it. This is why dangerous electric shocks can be obtained by the unwary from television receiver circuitry where voltages of several thousands of volts are present.

Energy stored in a dielectric

Energy is stored in all dielectrics whether or not the dielectric happens to be inside a capacitor. When considering the energy stored in a dielectric material it is often more convenient to express it in terms other than capacitance. The energy stored

$$W = CV^2/2 = \epsilon_r \epsilon_0 E^2 d^2 A/2d = DEAd/2$$

(since $D = \epsilon E$). Therefore,

$$\text{the energy stored in dielectric} = DE/2 \qquad \text{m}^3 \qquad (2.10)$$

$$= D^2/2\epsilon_0 \epsilon_r \qquad \text{J/m}^3 \qquad (2.11)$$

Example 2.10

A dielectric has an area of 20 cm^2, is 1 cm thick, and has a relative permittivity of 5. Calculate the energy stored in the dielectric when a voltage of 60 V is applied across it.

Solution

    Electric field strength $E = 60/(1 \times 10^{-2}) = 6\ kV/m.$
    Volume $= Ad = 20 \times 10^{-4} \times 1 \times 10^{-2} = 20 \times 10^{-6}\ m^3.$
    $D = \epsilon E = 5 \times 8.854 \times 10^{-12} \times 6000 = 265.62\ nC/m^3.$
    Energy stored $W = DE/2 \times$ volume
    $= (265.62 \times 10^{-9} \times 6000 \times 20 \times 10^{-6})/2 = 15.94\ nJ.$ (*Ans.*)

Capacitors in series

Figure 2.10 shows three capacitors C_1, C_2, and C_3 connected in series. The charge Q stored by each capacitor will be the same and so the voltage across C_1 is $V_1 = Q/C_1$; also the voltages across the other two capacitors are $V_2 = Q/C_2$ and $V_3 = Q/C_3$.

The total applied voltage is the sum of the individual capacitor voltages, i.e.,

$$V = V_1 + V_2 + V_3 = Q(1/C_1 + 1/C_2 + 1/C_3)$$
$$V/Q = 1/C_T = 1/C_1 + 1/C_2 + 1/C_3 \qquad (2.12)$$

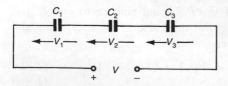

Fig. 2.10 Capacitors in series

The reciprocal of the total effective capacitance of three capacitors connected in series is the sum of the reciprocals of each capacitance. The effective capacitance will *always* be less than the capacitance of the smallest valued capacitor. When there are only two capacitors the effective capacitance is $1/C_T = 1/C_1 + 1/C_2 = (C_1 + C_2)/C_1 + C_2)$ and

$$C_T = C_1C_2/(C_1 + C_2) \tag{2.13}$$

Capacitors in parallel

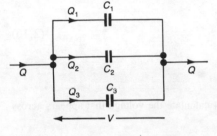

When three capacitors are connected in parallel, as shown by Fig. 2.11, the total charge Q supplied to the circuit divides into three separate charges Q_1, Q_2 and Q_3. Since the capacitors are connected in parallel they each have the same voltage across their terminals. Hence,

$$Q_1 = VC_1, \quad Q_2 = VC_2, \quad \text{and} \quad Q_3 = VC_3,$$
$$Q = Q_1 + Q_2 + Q_3 = V(C_1 + C_2 + C_3),$$
and $C_T = Q/V = C_1 + C_2 + C_3 \tag{2.14}$

Fig. 2.11 Capacitors in parallel

The total capacitance of two, or more, capacitors connected in parallel is equal to the sum of their individual capacitances.

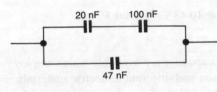

Fig. 2.12

Example 2.11

Calculate the total effective capacitance of the circuit given in Fig. 2.12.

Solution
The upper branch of the circuit has a capacitance of $(20 \times 100)/(20 + 100) = 16.67$ nF. Therefore, the total effective capacitance is $16.67 + 47 = 63.67$ nF. (*Ans.*)

Example 2.12

A 22 μF capacitor is charged from a 24 V power supply. The capacitor is then disconnected from the supply and connected in parallel with a 15 μF capacitor. Calculate (*a*) the voltage across the paralleled capacitors, (*b*) the energy stored in the 22 μF capacitor before it is connected to the other capacitor, and (*c*) the total energy stored after the connection has been made.

Solution
Charge stored $= 22 \times 10^{-6} \times 24 = 528$ μC. When the capacitors are connected in parallel the total capacitance is 37 μF.
(*a*) The total charge is unchanged so $528 \times 10^{-6} = 37 \times 10^{-6}$ V
or $V = (528 \times 10^{-6})/(37 \times 10^{-6}) = 14.27$ V. (*Ans.*)
(*b*) $W_{22} = 0.5 \times 22 \times 10^{-6} \times 24^2 = 6.34$ mJ. (*Ans.*)
(*c*) $W_{37} = 0.5 \times 37 \times 10^{-6} \times 14.27^2 = 3.77$ mJ. (*Ans.*)

The reduction in the stored energy arises because of the heat energy that is dissipated in the resistance of the circuit when current flows to make the two capacitor voltages equal to one another.

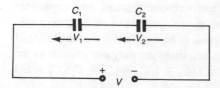
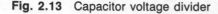

Fig. 2.13 Capacitor voltage divider

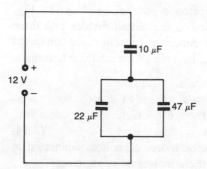

Fig. 2.14

Capacitor voltage divider

When a voltage is applied to a series circuit that consists of two, or more, capacitors connected in series the applied voltage will be divided into two, or more, parts that will appear across the individual capacitors. Fig. 2.13 shows two capacitors C_1 and C_2 connected in series and connected to a voltage supply of V volts. The total capacitance of the circuit is $C_T = C_1 C_2 / (C_1 + C_2)$ and so the charge is $Q = VC_1 C_2 / (C_1 + C_2)$. The voltage V_1 that appears across C_1 is equal to Q/C_1, or

$$V_1 = VC_2 / (C_1 + C_2) \tag{2.15}$$

Similarly,

$$V_2 = VC_1 / (C_1 + C_2) \tag{2.16}$$

Example 2.13

For the circuit given in Fig. 2.14 calculate the voltage that appears across the 10 μF capacitor.

Solution

The effective capacitance of the parallel capacitors is 69 μF and hence, from equation (2.15),
$$V_{10} = (12 \times 69) / (10 + 69) = 10.48 \text{ V.} \quad (Ans.)$$

Practical capacitors

A number of different types of capacitor are available which employ differing methods of construction and different dielectric materials. It is desirable to have some knowledge of the characteristics of the various types so that the correct capacitor(s) can be used in a circuit. Obviously the capacitance of a capacitor is its most important parameter but also of importance is its maximum working voltage. Amongst the other factors to be considered are its tolerance, stability, physical size, and leakage current.

Maximum working voltage

The maximum voltage that can be applied to the terminals of a capacitor without causing damage to it is always specified by the manufacturer. The specified limit is necessary to ensure that the electric field strength in the dielectric does not exceed the value at which the dielectric would break down and its insulating property would be lost. This figure, in V/m, is known as the *dielectric strength* and typical figures for some materials are given in Table 2.2.

The basic construction of a plastic capacitor is shown by Fig. 2.15. Two strips of aluminium foil are interleaved with two plastic strips and are then rolled up tightly. The terminals of the capacitor are

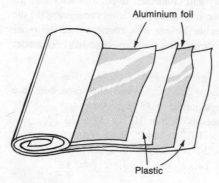

Fig. 2.15 Plastic capacitor

Table 2.2 Dielectric strength

Air	2×10^6 V/m	Paper	4×10^6 V
Polythene	60×10^6 V/m		
Mica	65×10^6 V/m	Waxed paper	25×10^6 V

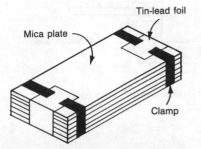

Fig. 2.16 Mica capacitor

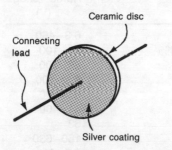

Fig. 2.17 Ceramic disc capacitor

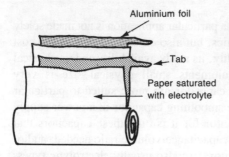

Fig. 2.18 Aluminium electrolytic capacitor

connected to the aluminium foil strips and then the whole assembly is placed within a case. The plastic employed may be polycarbonate, polyester, polypropylene, or polystyrene. An alternative method of construction for a plastic capacitor employs a plastic strip that has had aluminium sprayed onto one side of it before it is rolled up to form the capacitor.

The basic construction of a mica capacitor is shown by Fig. 2.16. A number of sheets of mica are coated with silver and then interleaved with thin sheets of copper foil and then these are held together by means of clamps. Ceramic capacitors come in at least four types, namely disc, dual-in-line, plate and tube. The ceramic disc capacitor, for example, is shown in Fig. 2.17 and it consists of a ceramic disc that has had a thin film of silver deposited onto its two faces. A connecting lead is soldered to each of the silver films before the capacitor is enclosed within a coating of enamel. The other types have a similar construction except that the ceramic is of different shape.

Whenever a large capacitance/volume ratio is wanted an electrolytic capacitor is employed. Two types are commonly used, the aluminium electrolytic, and the tantalum electrolytic, capacitors. In an aluminium electrolytic capacitor the dielectric is a thin layer of aluminium oxide that has been formed on the rough surface of a strip of aluminium foil. Aluminium oxide acts like a rectifier and it is able to withstand an applied voltage of one polarity only. The aluminium electrolytic capacitor is therefore a component that has one positive and one negative terminal. Non-polarized versions are also available; these have both electrodes with aluminium oxide layers of equal thickness. The treated strip of aluminium foil is then interleaved with porous paper that has been soaked in an electrolyte and an untreated strip of aluminium foil. The assembly is rolled up and put into an aluminium case with a lid and a rubber seal. Fig. 2.18 shows the construction of an aluminium electrolytic capacitor. The wet aluminium electrolytic capacitor is self-repairing if the dielectric should be punctured.

The construction of a solid tantalum electrolytic capacitor is shown by Fig. 2.19. The positive electrode consists of a slug of tantalum that has been coated with a layer of tantalum oxide and this layer acts as the dielectric. The negative electrode consists of a graphite layer that is in contact with a layer of silver. The dry electrolyte is deposited onto the tantalum oxide and then the assembly is placed inside a can and sealed.

Table 2.3 gives typical capacitance values, voltage ratings, and tolerances for the various kinds of capacitor.

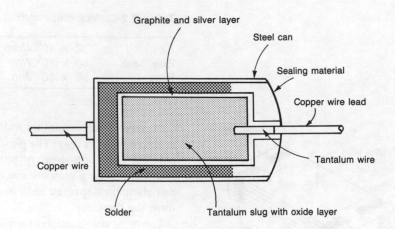

Fig. 2.19 Tantalum electrolytic capacitor

Table 2.3 Capacitor values and tolerances

Type	Capacitance range	Tolerance (%)	Rated voltage (V)
Aluminium electrolytic	1−4700 μF	±20%	6.3−450
Ceramic	2.2 pF−100 nF	−20 to +80%	63−100
Mica	10 pF−10 nF	±1%	63−100
Paper	1 nF−40 μF	±2%	6.3−100
Polycarbonate	100 pF−10 μF	±10%	63−400
Polyester	1 nF−2.2 μF	±20%	64−400
Polypropylene	100 pF−10 nF	±5%	63
Polystyrene	10 pF−8.2 nF	±1%	160−630
Tantalum electrolytic	0.1−150 μF	±20%	6.3−35

The choice of capacitor for a particular application is not made solely on the electrical characteristics, but also on such factors as the cost of the component, its reliability, its ready availability and its physical size. In many modern equipments small physical size is very important. Certain types of capacitor are more suited to particular applications than others: the smoothing capacitor in a power supply will be an electrolytic capacitor for it is only these capacitors that are able to provide the large capacitance/volume ratio needed; audio-frequency decoupling capacitors are also usually electrolytic types. Capacitors are frequently employed to couple one part of a circuit to another, or to couple the input terminal of a circuit to its source, or the output terminals to the load and one of the plastic capacitors would probably be chosen. Radio-frequency decoupling capacitors are most often either plastic or ceramic capacitors while tuning capacitors are usually mica, ceramic, or polystyrene types. Some capacitors are made specifically for use with printed circuits and these are often either ceramic dual-in-line or polyester types.

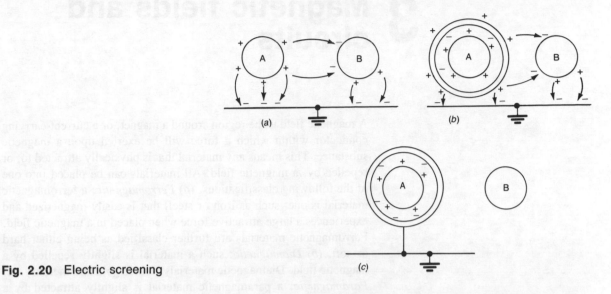

Fig. 2.20 Electric screening

Electric screening

It is frequently necessary to screen, or shield, a conductor or a part of a circuit from an external electric field. Figure 2.20(a) shows two conductors, A and B, that are situated above an earthed conducting surface. If conductor A is at a positive potential an equal magnitude, opposite polarity, charge will be induced both onto conductor B and the conducting surface. The charge induced into conductor B will also induce a charge onto the conducting surface as shown. Since the conducting surface is earthed the charges induced into it leak away.

If conductor A is enclosed within a hollow conducting screen as shown by Fig. 2.20(b) a negative charge will be induced onto the inner surface of the screen. This produces a positive charge on the outer surface of the screen and this will induce charges onto both conductor B and the conducting surface. If the hollow screen around conductor A is earthed, as shown by Fig. 2.20(c), the positive charge that appears on the outer surface of the screen leaks away and there will be zero charge induced onto conductor B.

An earthed screen can therefore be employed to prevent an electric field setting up a p.d. between two nearby conductors. The screen is usually made from a thin sheet of copper.

3 Magnetic fields and circuits

A magnetic field is the region around a magnet, or a current-carrying conductor within which a force will be exerted upon a magnetic substance. This means any material that is physically attracted to, or repelled by, a magnetic field. All materials can be placed into one of the following classifications: (*a*) *Ferromagnetic*; a ferromagnetic material is one, such as iron or steel, that is easily magnetized and experiences a large attractive force when placed in a magnetic field. Ferromagnetic materials are further classified as being either hard or soft. (*b*) *Diamagnetic*; such a material is slightly repelled by a magnetic field. Diamagnetic materials include gold and mercury. (*c*) *Paramagnetic*; a paramagnetic material is slightly attracted by a magnetic field. This type includes aluminium and copper. Both diamagnetic and paramagnetic materials are generally classified as non-magnetic materials.

The three-dimensional magnetic field is normally considered, in order to obtain a convenient pictorial representation of the field, to consist of a number of *lines of magnetic flux*. The direction of the flux lines at any point within the magnetic field indicate the direction in which a force would be exerted upon a North pole at that point. The determination of the field pattern for particular cases makes use of the following rules that the flux lines must always obey: (*a*) Every line of flux must form a closed loop that is known as a flux linkage. (*b*) The lines of flux cannot cross one another. (*c*) Flux lines must always take the shortest possible path. (*d*) Parallel lines of flux in the same direction are mutually repellent and tend to move away from one another. The complete path followed by a group of flux lines is known as a *magnetic circuit*; this may often consist mainly of air but whenever a magnetic circuit is designed as a part of a system that is to make full use of the forces exerted by magnetic fields, such as a relay or an electric motor, the magnetic circuit will mainly use ferromagnetic materials.

Magnetic fields

Figure 3.1 shows the magnetic fields produced by two bar magnets. All permanent magnets have two poles that are always labelled as North and South and Fig. 3.1(*a*) shows the magnetic field that is produced by a bar magnet. The lines of flux leave the North pole of the magnet and form a closed loop by entering the magnet's South pole. The direction of the flux lines is from North to South. When two such bar magnets are placed in close proximity to one another

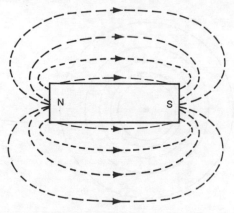

(a)

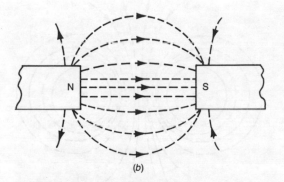

(b)

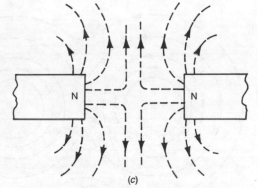

(c)

Fig. 3.1 Magnetic fields; (a) of a
bar magnet, (b) between unlike
poles, and (c) between like poles

the magnetic field pattern that is set up will depend upon whether
the two North (or South) poles are adjacent to one another or whether
a North pole is adjacent to a South pole. Figure 3.1(b) shows the
magnetic field for two bar magnets that have their North and South
poles adjacent to one another; the flux lines go from the North pole
of one magnet to the South pole of the other magnet but since the
flux lines are mutually repellent very few flux lines follow the shortest,
direct path. As can be seen, many of the flux lines follow a curved
path from one magnet to the other. Since the flux lines always attempt
to shorten their length there is an attractive force exerted between
the two magnets. When, Fig. 3.1(c), two North poles are adjacent
to one another no flux lines go from one magnet to the other; the
flux lines from each pole repel one another and follow the paths shown.
There is now a repellent force exerted on the two magnets and they
will attempt to move away from one another. Poles of opposite polarity
always attract one another and poles of the same polarity repel one
another.

When a current flows in a conductor a magnetic field is set up
around that conductor. This field behaves in a way that is

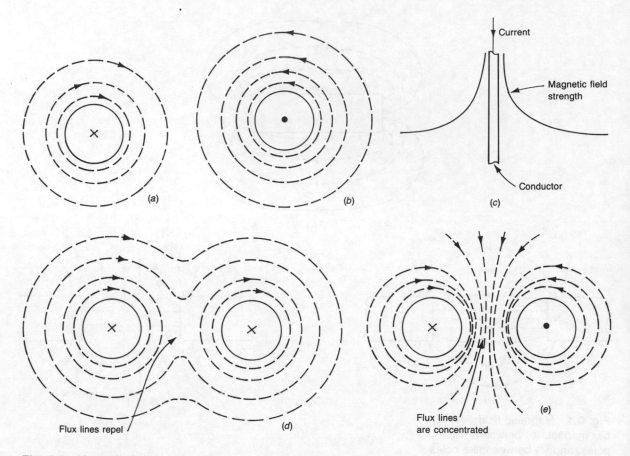

Fig. 3.2 Magnetic fields; around a conductor carrying current (*a*) into the paper, (*b*) out of the paper, and between two conductors carrying currents (*d*) in the same direction, (*e*) in opposite directions. (*c*) shows how the magnetic field strength varies with distance from the conductor

indistinguishable from the magnetic field produced by a permanent magnet but the field is not permanent and disappears immediately the current ceases to flow. The direction of the field is determined by the direction in which the current flows. When, Fig. 3.2(*a*), the current flows in the direction into the paper the magnetic field is in the clockwise direction. Conversely, Fig. 3.2(*b*), when the current flows in the direction out of the paper the magnetic field produced is in the anti-clockwise direction. Note that the direction into the paper is signified by a cross and the direction out of the paper is signified by a dot. The intensity of the magnetic field is inversely proportional to the distance from the axis of the conductor and this is shown by Fig. 3.2(*c*). The reduction in field strength can be represented by drawing concentric circles with increased spacing as the distance from the conductor is increased. When two current-carrying conductors are adjacent to one another the magnetic field distribution between them will depend upon the relative directions of the current in each of the conductors. Figure 3.2(*d*) shows the magnetic field pattern produced when two conductors are both carrying a current in the same direction, here assumed to be in the direction into the paper. If the current in the right-hand conductor has its direction reversed so that

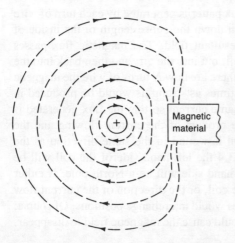

Fig. 3.3 Effect of magnetic material in a magnetic field

it is out of the paper the magnetic field produced is of the form shown by Fig. 3.2.(*e*). When the two currents flow in the same direction there will be a force of attraction between the two conductors and when the currents flow in opposite directions there will be a repelling force exerted on the conductors.

If an object made from a magnetic material is placed into the magnetic field surrounding a current-carrying conductor the flux pattern will be distorted. The lines of flux will bend in order to pass through the magnetic material and there will be a concentrated field in the material. This is shown by Fig. 3.3. The magnetic field produced by the current flowing in a single conductor can be increased if the conductor is bent to form a single turn of wire as shown by Fig. 3.4(*a*). If the turn is viewed from the top and the section AA through the widest part is considered the view will be as shown by Fig. 3.4(*b*). The current in the left-hand side of the turn is flowing in the direction out of the paper and so the magnetic field that it produces is in the anti-clockwise direction. At the same time the current in the right-hand side of the turn is flowing in the direction into the paper and so the magnetic field around this side of the turn will be in the clockwise direction. This means that the flux lines are entering the turn of wire from the left and leave it from the right as shown by Fig. 3.4(*c*). Therefore the left-hand side of the turn acts as a South pole and the right-hand side acts like a North pole of a magnet. The magnetic poles would, of course, interchange their positions if the direction of the current were to be reversed.

The magnetic field can be still further increased if a large number of turns of wire are wound on a hollow insulating former to form

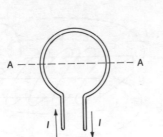
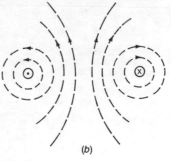
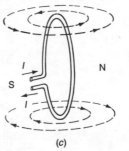

Fig. 3.4 Magnetic field due to a single turn of wire, showing three views

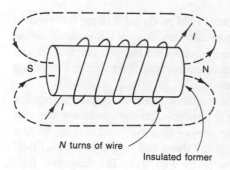

Fig. 3.5 Magnetic field due to a coil

Magnetic circuits

a coil as in Fig. 3.5. The flux patterns generated by each turn of wire all act in the same direction down the entire length of the inside of the coil to give a larger resultant field. The magnetic flux passes through the inside of the coil, out into the air, and then back into the other end of the coil. Since there are now N turns of wire the magnetic field that is produced is N times as strong as would be produced in a single turn carrying the same current so that the flux generated is directly proportional to the product of the current flowing and the number of turns. If the coil is wound in the same direction as the single turn shown in Fig. 3.4 the left-hand side of the coil will be a South pole and the right-hand side will be a North pole. If either the direction of winding the coil, or the direction of the current flow were to be reversed the poles would interchange positions. Of course, switching off the current would cause the magnetic field to disappear.

If a core made from a magnetic material is introduced into the space inside the former, as shown by Fig. 3.6, a greater total magnetic flux will be produced and the flux will be concentrated within the core. An even stronger magnetic field will be produced, for the same current—turns product, if the magnetic core were to be extended to give the magnetic circuit shown in Fig. 3.7. The core now provides a path for the magnetic flux to pass from the North end of the coil to the South end. Besides giving an increased flux the flux is concentrated at the air gap.

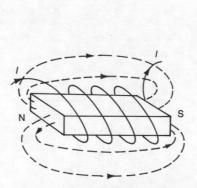

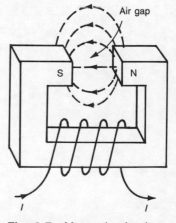

Fig. 3.6 Use of a magnetic core   **Fig. 3.7** Magnetic circuit

Magnetic flux and flux density

Magnetic flux Φ is a representation of the strength of the magnetic field and it is measured in a unit known as the weber (Wb). The weber is a rather large unit for most practical purposes and either the milliweber (mWb) or the microweber (μWb) is generally used. A figure for the magnetic flux in a magnetic circuit gives no indication

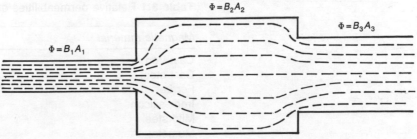

Fig. 3.8 Magnetic flux density

at all of the concentration of that flux. This is shown by Fig. 3.8 which shows a series magnetic circuit having three different cross-sectional areas A_1, A_2, and A_3. The flux will be the same in all parts of the circuit, similar to the current in a series electrical circuit, but clearly the flux density is not constant. The flux density is greatest in the left-hand part of the circuit, least in the middle part of the circuit, and somewhere in between in the right-hand part of the circuit. The *magnetic flux density B* is the magnetic flux per square metre in tesla (T), i.e.,

$$B = \Phi/A \qquad \text{T} \tag{3.1}$$

$$\text{or} \quad \Phi = BA \qquad \text{Wb} \tag{3.2}$$

where A is the area in square metres through which the flux passes at right angles. If the flux is not normal to the plane considered but is at an angle θ to the plane, then

$$\Phi = BA \sin \theta \qquad \text{Wb} \tag{3.3}$$

The unit of flux density is such that a conductor carrying a current of 1 A at right-angles to the magnetic field will have a force of 1 N/m exerted upon it.

Example 3.1

Calculate the flux density when a flux of 1 mWb passes through an area of 10 cm^2 at (*a*) right-angles, and (*b*) at 60° to the area.

Solution
    (*a*) Flux density $B = (1 \times 10^{-3})/(10 \times 10^{-4}) = 1$ T.   (*Ans.*)
    (*b*) Flux density $B = (1 \times 10^{-3})/(10 \times 10^{-4}) \times \sin 60°$
                         $= 1.16$ T.   (*Ans.*)

Permeability

When the space within the coil shown in Fig. 3.5 was filled by a ferromagnetic core the flux density within the coil was considerably increased (Fig. 3.6). The multiplying factor by which the flux density is increased is known as the *relative permeability* μ_r of the material. The *absolute permeability* of the material is the product $\mu_r \mu_0$, where

Table 3.1 Relative permeabilities of magnetic materials

Magnetic material	Relative permeability
Cast iron	200
Cast steel	700
Ferrite	4 800
Iron–silicon	3 500
Mild steel	600
Mumetal	6 000
Nickel–iron	100 000
Nickel–iron–copper	80 000
Nickel–iron–copper–chromium	75 000
Nickel–iron–cobalt	10 000
Radiometal	600
Silicon steel	4 500
Stalloy	4 000

μ_0 is the *permeability of free space*. The value of μ_0 is $4\pi \times 10^{-7}$ Henry/metre and it is, strictly speaking, the permeability of a vacuum. In practice, however, μ_0 is also taken to be the permeability of air. Some typical values of relative permeability are given in Table 3.1.

It should be noted that all magnetic materials are non-linear in their behaviour and this means that a material does not have a constant value of permeability. The permeability will vary with the flux density, with the temperature, and, if an alternating current is used, with the frequency of the signal.

Ferrites are non-metallic materials consisting of a compound of iron oxide, zinc, and nickel particles held together by a binding agent. They have a high resistivity and high permeability; the μ_r figure in the table is the mean of a wide range of possible values, such as 200 to 10 000.

Magnetomotive force

To establish a magnetic flux in a magnetic circuit a magnetomotive force (m.m.f.) must be applied. The m.m.f. is the work done in joules in moving a flux of 1 Wb once around a magnetic circuit. An m.m.f. is applied to a magnetic circuit by passing a current through a coil of wire wound around the circuit or a part of it. The current sets up a magnetic field around each turn in the coil and the magnitude of the resultant magnetic field is directly proportional to both the current and to the number of turns. Thus,

$$\text{m.m.f. } F = NI \quad \text{A} \tag{3.4}$$

Example 3.2

Calculate the m.m.f. produced by a current of 25 mA flowing in a coil of wire having 2000 turns.

Solution

m.m.f. $F = 2000 \times 25 \times 10^{-3} = 50$ A.   (*Ans.*)

Magnetic field strength

Two magnetic circuits might have the same m.m.f. applied to them but have quite different magnetic fluxes set up because the lengths of the two circuits were different. The magnetic field strength H takes account of the length of the magnetic path, i.e.,

$$H = NI/l \quad \text{A/m} \tag{3.5}$$

where l is the length of the magnetic path in metres.

Example 3.3

Calculate the magnetic field strength when the m.m.f. in Example 3.2 is applied to a magnetic circuit of length (*a*) 0.025 m and (*b*) 0.5 m.

Solution

(*a*) $H = 50/0.025 = 2000$ A/m.   (*Ans.*)
(*b*) $H = 50/0.5 = 100$ A/m.   (*Ans.*)

Flux density B is directly proportional to the magnetic field strength H, the constant of proportionality being the absolute permeability of the magnetic material. Thus

$$B = \mu_r \mu_0 H \quad \text{T} \tag{3.6}$$

Example 3.4

An iron ring has a mean diameter of 0.4 m and a cross-sectional area of 5×10^{-4} m^2. A coil with 3000 turns is wound on the ring. Calculate the current that must flow in the coil for a flux of 0.5 mWb to be set up in the ring. The relative permeability μ_r is 800.

Solution

Flux density $B = \Phi/A = (0.5 \times 10^{-3})/(5 \times 10^{-4}) = 1$ T.

$$H = B/\mu_0 \mu_r = NI/l.$$

Therefore, $I = Bl/N\mu_0 \mu_r = (1 \times \pi \times 0.4)/(3000 \times 4\pi \times 10^{-7} \times 800)$
$$= 417 \text{ mA}. \quad (\text{*Ans.*})$$

The magnetization curve

The magnetization curve of a ferromagnetic material shows how the flux density in the material varies with change in the applied magnetic field strength.

Consider a magnetic material that is initially unmagnetized and that has a magnetic field strength H applied to it. If the magnetic field

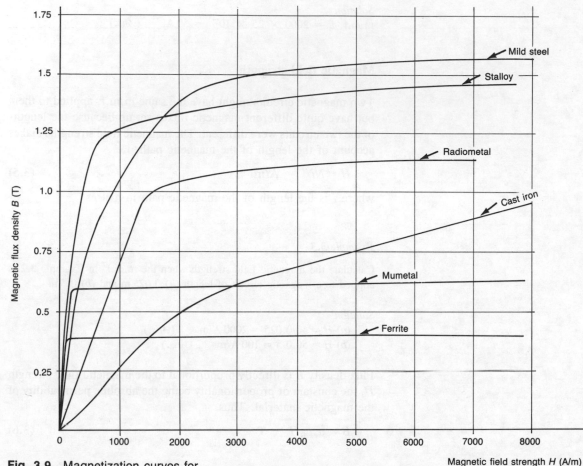

Fig. 3.9 Magnetization curves for different ferromagnetic materials

strength is gradually increased the flux density will, at first, increase as well. Initially the flux density increases rapidly but then its rate of increase falls and eventually there is very little increase in the flux density with further increase in the magnetic field strength. Once this happens the material is said to be *magnetically saturated*. The small increase in the flux density that occurs after saturation has been reached is entirely due to the increase in the current. Figure 3.9 shows typical magnetization curves for some different magnetic materials.

At any point on a magnetization curve the relative permeability of the magnetic material can be determined from the corresponding values of the magnetic field strength and the flux density.

Example 3.5

Table 3.2 gives data for a specimen of mild steel. Plot the magnetization curve for the material and then use it to find the relative permeability of the material when the magnetic field strength is equal to (*a*) 600 A/m, (*b*) 1500 A/m, (*c*) 3500 A/m, and (*d*) 5000 A/m. Plot μ_r against H.

Table 3.2

Magnetic field strength (A/m)	200	500	1000	2000	3000	4000	5000	5500	6000	6500	7000
Flux density (T)	0.6	0.9	1.15	1.45	1.58	1.66	1.7	1.72	1.73	1.74	1.75

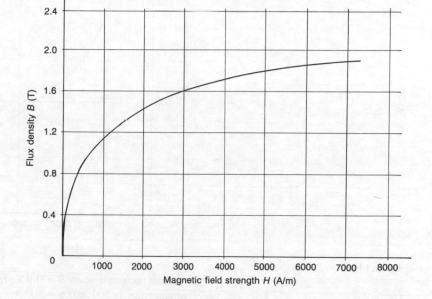

Fig. 3.10

Solution

The required magnetization curve is shown in Fig. 3.10. From the graph:

    (a) When $H = 600$, $B = 1$ T; $\mu_r = B/\mu_0 H = 1326$.   (*Ans.*)

    (b) $H = 1500$, $B = 1.32$ T; $\mu_r = 700$.   (*Ans.*)

    (c) $H = 3500$, $B = 1.66$ T; $\mu_r = 377$.   (*Ans.*)

    (d) $H = 5000$, $B = 1.7$ T; $\mu_r = 270$.   (*Ans.*)

Plotting these values against H gives the graph shown in Fig. 3.11. Clearly, the relative permeability does not have a constant value but, instead, it varies considerably with the value of the magnetic field strength.

Example 3.6

A magnetic circuit made from the material whose magnetization curve is given in Fig. 3.10 has a mean length of 0.6 m and a cross-sectional area of 10 cm², and it is wound with 1000 turns of wire. There is an air gap of 2.5 mm width and a flux density of 0.9 T is to be set up in this air gap. Calculate the required current in the coil.

Solution

For the air gap, $H = B/\mu_0 = 0.9/(4\pi \times 10^{-7}) = 716.2 \times 10^3$ A/m. The m.m.f. required to produce this is equal to $716.2 \times 10^3 \times 2.5 \times 10^{-3}$ $= 1790.5$ A.

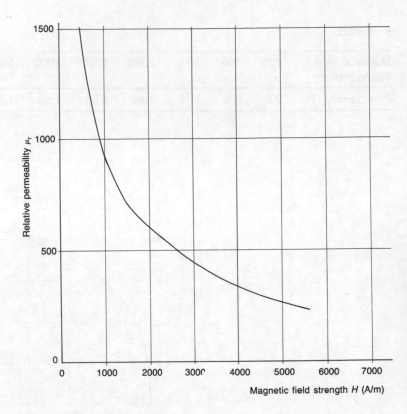

Fig. 3.11

From the graph when $B = 0.9$ T, $H = 500$ A/m. The required m.m.f to produce this is $500 \times 0.6 = 300$ A.

The total required m.m.f. $= 1790.5 + 300 = 2090.5$ A.

Therefore, required current in coil $= 2090.5/1000 = 2.09$ A.   (*Ans.*)

Incremental permeability

The incremental permeability of a magnetic material is the permeability that is offered to an a.c. signal. Usually the incremental permeability has a different value from the static permeability. Consider Fig. 3.12 which shows the magnetization curve of a magnetic material; the static permeability of the material is found from the corresponding values of flux density B and magnetic field strength H, e.g., $\mu = B/H$. The incremental permeability is defined as dB/dH, i.e., slope of the tangent to the B/H curve. The incremental permeability changes markedly at different points on the curve and falls to zero when magnetic saturation has occurred.

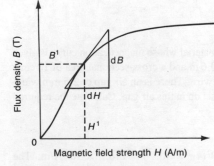

Fig. 3.12 Incremental permeability

Example 3.7

Calculate the incremental permeability of the material whose magnetization curve is given in Fig. 3.10 at the points (*a*) $H = 500$ A, (*b*) $H = 3000$ A, and (*c*) $H = 6500$ A.

Solution

Taking $H = 250$ A increments either side of each point:

    (*a*) $dB/dH = (1.08 - 0.72)/(500 \times 4\pi \times 10^{-7}) = 573.$ (*Ans.*)

    (*b*) $dB/dH = (1.63 - 1.57)/(500 \times 4\pi \times 10^{-7}) = 96.$ (*Ans.*)

    (*c*) $dB/dH = (1.9 - 1.86)/(500 \times 4\pi \times 10^{-7}) = 64.$ (*Ans.*)

Reluctance

A magnetic circuit can always be regarded as being analogous to an electrical circuit and calculations on series. parallel, and series–parallel circuits carried in a similar manner, i.e., the magnetic equivalents of Ohm's law, Kirchhoff's law, resistors in series, etc., can be used. The analogies between magnetic and electrical circuits are listed in Table 3.3.

The parameters are analogous, since identical mathematical relationships exist between them, but they are equivalents since they refer to entirely different quantities. It can be seen from the table that magnetic reluctance is analogous to electrical resistance. This means that

$$\text{Reluctance } S = \text{m.m.f./flux} = NI/\Phi \quad \text{A/Wb.} \tag{3.7}$$

$$= Hl/BA = l/\mu_0 \mu_r A \quad \text{A/Wb.} \tag{3.8}$$

The *inductance* L (p. 55) of a circuit is given by $L = N\Phi/I$, or $\Phi = LI/N$. Substituting this relationship into equation (3.7) gives

$$S = N^2/L \quad H^{-1} \tag{3.9}$$

The reciprocal of reluctance is known as permeance.

Example 3.8

A coil has 2000 turns of wire and a current of 100 mA passing through it produces a magnetic flux of 1 mWb. Calculate (*a*) the inductance of the coil, and (*b*) the reluctance of the magnetic circuit.

Solution

    (*a*) $L = (2000 \times 1 \times 10^{-3})/(100 \times 10^{-3}) = 20$ H.   (*Ans.*)

    (*b*) $S = 2000^2/20 = 200 \times 10^3$ A/Wb.   (*Ans.*)

Table 3.3 Magnetic/electrical analogues

m.m.f. ($F = NI$)	A	e.m.f. (V)	V
flux (Φ)	Wb	current (I)	A
flux density (B)	T	current density (J)	A/m^2
magnetic field strength ($H = NI/l$)	A/m	electric field strength (E)	V/m
reluctance (S)	A/Wb or H^{-1}	resistance (R)	Ω
Absolute permeability (ϵ)	H/m	conductivity (σ)	S/m

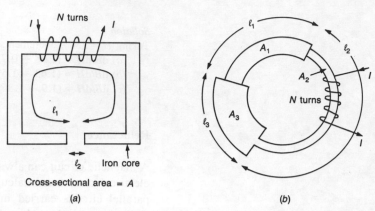

Fig. 3.13 Two series magnetic circuits

N turns

I I

ℓ_1

ℓ_2 Iron core

Cross-sectional area = A

(a)

ℓ_1

A_1

ℓ_2

A_2

N turns

I

ℓ_3 A_3

I

(b)

Series magnetic circuits

A series magnetic circuit has the same flux in all parts of the circuit and two examples are shown by Figs 3.13(a) and (b). In circuit (a) the iron core will have a reluctance of $S_1 = l_1/\mu_r\mu_0 A_1$ and the air gap will have a reluctance of $S_2 = l_2/\mu_0 A_1$, assuming the cross-sectional area of the air gap is the same as that of the rest of the circuit, i.e., assuming that fringing is negligible. The total m.m.f. required to set up a wanted flux density in the air gap is the sum of the m.m.f.s needed to set up that flux in the iron core and in the air gap, i.e., $F_T = F_1 + F_2$. Hence,

$$F_T/\Phi = S_T = S_1 + S_2 \tag{3.10}$$

The total reluctance of two, or more, reluctances in series is the algebraic sum of the individual reluctances. In Fig 3.13(b) the reluctances of the three parts of the circuit are $S_1 = l_1/\mu_0\mu_r A_1$, $S_2 = l_2/\mu_0\mu_r A_2$, and $S_3 = l_3/\mu_0\mu_r A_3$ respectively. The total reluctance is $S_T = S_1 + S_2 + S_3$.

Example 3.9

A mild-steel ring has a cross-sectional area of 5 cm^2, a mean length of 62 cm, and an air gap of length 2.5 mm. There is a coil of 1000 turns wound on the ring. Calculate the current needed to produce a flux of 500 μWb in the air gap. The magnetization curve for mild steel is shown by Fig. 3.10. Perform the calculation (a) using the curve, and (b) using the reluctances of the magnetic circuit.

Solution

(a) Flux density $B = (500 \times 10^{-6})/(5 \times 10^{-4}) = 1$ T. From Fig. 3.10, the magnetic field strength H is 650 A/m and so for the steel ring, m.m.f. $F = 650 \times 61.75 \times 10^{-2} = 401.4$ A.

For the air gap, $H = B/\mu_0 = 1/(4\pi \times 10^{-7}) = 795.8 \times 10^3$ A/m. m.m.f. $= 795.8 \times 10^3 \times 2.5 \times 10^{-3} = 1989.5$ A.

Total m.m.f. $= 401.4 + 1989.4 = 2391$ A, and current needed $= 2.39$ A.   (*Ans.*)

(*b*) Flux density $B = 1$ T and $\mu_r = B/\mu_0 H = 1/(4\pi \times 10^{-7} \times 650) = 1224$.

The reluctance S_s of the mild steel ring is $S_s = (61.75 \times 10^{-2})/(4\pi \times 10^{-7} \times 1224 \times 5 \times 10^{-4}) = 0.8 \times 10^6$ A/Wb.

Reluctance of air gap $= (2.5 \times 10^{-3})/(4\pi \times 10^{-7} \times 5 \times 10^{-4}) = 3.98 \times 10^6$ A/Wb.

The total reluctance is $S_T = (0.8 + 3.98) \times 10^6 = 4.78 \times 10^6$ A/Wb. Therefore, the m.m.f. needed $= F_T = 4.78 \times 10^6 \times 500 \times 10^{-6} = 2389$ A and the current required $= 2389/1000 = 2.39$ A.   (*Ans.*)

Calculations on magnetic circuits that are based upon the reluctances of the different parts of a circuit depend upon a knowledge of the relative permeability of the magnetic material. But, as Fig. 3.11 has shown, an assumption of a constant permeability is incorrect. It is therefore better to base magnetic circuit calculations upon the application of the magnetization curve for the material.

Magnetic leakage and fringing

In practice, not all of the flux predicted in a magnetic core by a magnetic circuit calculation will actually pass through the air gap. Instead, there are three reasons why some flux is 'lost'.

1. When a current flows in a coil an m.m.f. is induced into the magnetic circuit which causes a magnetic flux to be set up but some of this flux leaks around the in-air path in parallel with the core. This has been labelled as the *coil leakage flux* in Fig. 3.14.

2. Some more of the flux, known as the *core leakage flux*, will leak from one part of the magnetic circuit to another part.

3. In addition, not all of the flux that reaches the air gap will pass directly from one side of the gap to the other side. Some of the flux follows a curved path because of the mutually repelling action of the flux lines; this *fringing*, shown in the figure as the fringing flux, effectively increases the cross-sectional area of the air gap and in so doing reduces the flux density in the gap. The wider the air gap is the greater will be the amount of fringing that occurs.

The combined effect of leakage and fringing is to reduce the amount of work that the magnetic system is able to do. Most, if not all, magnetic circuits are designed to keep these undesirable effects as small as possible and they are often small enough to be neglected. If necessary, the effective cross-sectional area of the air gap can be estimated and used to take account of the fringing effect.

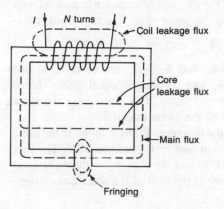

Fig. 3.14 Leakage flux and fringing

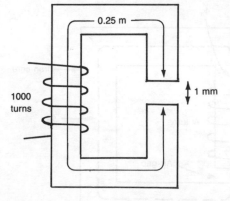

Fig. 3.15

Example 3.10

The core shown in Fig. 3.15 has a mean length of 0.25 cm and an air gap of width 1 mm. Calculate the current that must flow in the coil to produce a flux density of 0.8 T in the air gap. There is a 20% loss of flux due to leakage and the relative permeability of the core material is 600.

Solution
In the air gap $H = B/\mu_0\mu_r = 0.8/(4\pi \times 10^{-7}) = 636620$ A/m.
The m.m.f. in the air gap is $Hl = 636620 \times 10^{-3} = 637.62$ A.
Flux density in iron = $5/4 \times 0.8 = 1$ T. The m.m.f. for the iron is $Hl = Bl/\mu_0\mu_r = (1 \times 0.25)/(600 \times 4\pi \times 10^{-7}) = 331.57$ A.
Total m.m.f. = $637.62 + 331.57 = 969.19$ A.
Current needed = 0.97 A.   (*Ans.*)

Parallel magnetic circuits

Figure 3.16 shows a parallel magnetic circuit. The centre limb has N turns of wire wound around it and a current of I amps flowing in this winding produces a flux Φ_T in the centre limb. This flux is equal to NI/S_T, where S_T is the total reluctance of the circuit. The left-hand, and right-hand limbs of the magnetic circuit are in parallel with one another and so they have the same m.m.f. across them, i.e.,

$$NI = S_T\Phi_T = S_1\Phi_1 = S_3\Phi_2, \quad \text{and} \quad \Phi_T = \Phi_1 + \Phi_2.$$

Obviously, the two fluxes Φ_1 and Φ_2 will only be equal to one another if the reluctances S_1 and S_2 are of equal value. Since $S = l/\mu A$ this means that the two outer limbs must have the same dimensions if they are made of the same material.

The effective reluctance of the two outer limbs is found in the same way as the effective resistance of two resistors in parallel. The flux Φ_1 in the left-hand limb is NI/S_1 and the flux Φ_2 in the right-hand limb is NI/S_2. The total flux Φ_T is the sum of the outer limb fluxes, i.e., $\Phi_T = \Phi_1 + \Phi_2$. Hence,

$$\text{m.m.f.}/S_T = \text{m.m.f.}/(1/S_1 + 1/S_2)$$
$$\text{or} \qquad 1/S_T = 1/S_1 + 1/S_2 \tag{3.11}$$

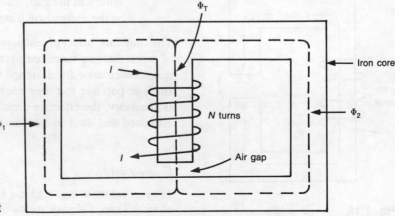

Fig. 3.16 Parallel magnetic circuit

The equation can be extended to any number of reluctances connected in parallel. When there are only two reluctances in parallel the equation can be more conveniently be written as

$$S_T = S_1 S_2/(S_1 + S_2) \tag{3.12}$$

Example 3.11

The magnetic circuit shown in Fig. 3.16 has the following dimensions: length of centre arm = 0.2 m, length of air gap = 2 mm, mean length of both outer arms = 0.6 m, cross-sectional area of all parts = 25 cm^2. Calculate the current that must flow in the windings to produce a flux of 4 mWb in the air gap. Use the magnetization curve of Fig. 3.10.

Solution

The flux density B in the centre limb is $(4 \times 10^{-3})/(25 \times 10^{-4}) = 1.6$ T. The flux density in each of the outer limbs is therefore 0.8 T. From the curve the magnetic field strength H in the centre limb is 3000 A/m and in the outer limbs is 375 A/m. The magnetic field strength in the air gap is $H_a = B/\mu_0 A = 1.6/(4\pi \times 10^7) = 1273 \times 10^3$ A/m. The m.m.f.s required in each part of the circuit are: centre limb, $3000 \times 0.2 = 600$ A; each outer limb, 375×0.6 m = 225 A; air gap, $1273 \times 10^3 \times 2 \times 10^{-3} = 2544$ A. The total m.m.f. = 600 + 450 + 2544 = 3594 A, and hence the required current in the winding is 3594/1000 = 3.59 A. (*Ans.*)

Example 3.12

Figure 3.17 shows the magnetic circuit of an inductor. The iron has a relative permeability of 800. Calculate the current that must flow in the windings to produce a flux in the air gap of 0.6 mWb.

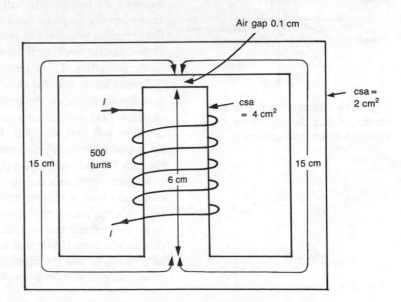

Fig. 3.17

Solution

For the centre limb, m.m.f. $= \Phi S = (0.6 \times 10^{-3} \times 6 \times 10^{-2})/(4\pi \times 10^{-7} \times 800 \times 4 \times 10^{-4}) = 89.5$ A.

For either outer limb m.m.f. $= (0.3 \times 10^{-3} \times 15 \times 10^{-2})/(4\pi \times 10^{-7} \times 800 \times 2 \times 10^{-4}) = 223.8$ A.

For the air gap m.m.f. $= Hl = Bl/\mu_0 = \Phi l/\mu_0 A = (0.6 \times 10^{-3} \times 10^{-3})/(4\pi \times 10^{-7} \times 4 \times 10^{-4}) = 1193.7$ A. The total m.m.f. $= 89.5 + 223.8 + 1193.7 = 1507$ A.

Current needed $= 1507/500 = 3.01$ A.   (*Ans.*)

The hysteresis loop

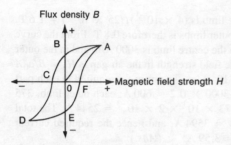

Fig. 3.18   Hysteresis loop

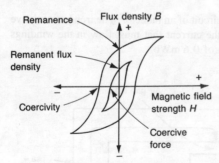

Fig. 3.19   Illustrating the terms remanent flux density, remanence, coercive force and coercivity

The hysteresis loop of an initially unmagnetized magnetic material is obtained by taking a sample of the material through one complete cycle of magnetization and plotting the corresponding values of the magnetic field strength and the flux density. Consider the hysteresis loop shown in Fig. 3.18. When the magnetic field strength is first increased from zero the flux density will also increase, following the path 0A. Initially the rate of increase in the flux density is large but it becomes smaller and very nearly constant over most of the path up to point A. If magnetic saturation is reached the rate of increase of the flux density becomes very nearly zero. When the magnetic field strength reaches its maximum value the flux density will have attained its maximum value also. If, now, the magnetic field strength is reduced the flux density will not retrace its original path 0A but, instead, it will follow the curve AB. The flux density will *not* have fallen to zero when the magnetic field strength has become zero. The flux density remaining, i.e., 0B, is the residual magnetism and it is known as the *remanent flux density*, or if the material has been taken into saturation, as the *remanence*.

When the magnetic field strength is increased in the negative direction the flux density will follow the path BC and will become zero when the magnetic field strength is equal to 0C. The magnetic field strength necessary to reduce the flux density to zero is known as the *coercive force*, or if the material had been taken into saturation as the *coercivity*. These terms are illustrated by Fig. 3.19.

Further increase in the negative magnetic field strength causes the flux density to follow the path CD and if the positive and negative magnetic field strength are of equal magnitude the two maximum flux densities will also be equal. If the magnetic field strength is now decreased from its negative value to zero the flux density will follow the path DE and, once again there will be some residual magnetism.

Magnetic materials that are easy to magnetize (magnetically soft materials) have a narrow hysteresis loop; other magnetically hard materials that are not easily magnetized have a much wider hysteresis loop. A magnetic material that is used in a digital system to store data should have a hysteresis loop that is as near rectangular in shape as possible so that the change-over from one magnetic state to the other occupies as short a time as possible. Work must be done to take a magnetic material through a cycle of magnetization and so some energy is dissipated. The hysteresis losses are directly proportional to the area of the hysteresis loop.

Air gaps

An air gap in a magnetic circuit is often necessary so that the system is able to move and do work. Although the length of the gap is usually very small compared to the length of the rest of the circuit it still has the larger value of reluctance. The length of the air gap must be accurately known since even a small error in length will have a marked effect upon the calculated values of flux and flux density. On the other hand an error in the length of the rest of the magnetic circuit will have little effect upon the calculated values.

The inclusion of an air gap into a magnetic circuit also makes the circuit have a more linear relationship between the m.m.f. and the resulting magnetic flux.

Magnetic materials

Materials that can be magnetized are known as ferromagnetic materials and these, in turn, are generally known as either hard or soft materials. Magnetically hard materials are ones that have high values of remanence and coercivity, a wide hysteresis loop, and (unfortunately) a high hysteresis loss and are suitable for use as permanent magnets. Most permanent-magnet materials consist of some kind of iron or steel alloy with one, or more, of aluminium, cobalt, copper and nickel, e.g., alni is an alloy of iron, aluminium and nickel, and anico is an alloy of iron, aluminium, nickel and cobalt.

Magnetically soft materials are suitable for use as electromagnets and have (a) high permeability, (b) high resistivity, (c) low remanence, (d) low coercivity, (e) low saturation level, (f) a narrow hysteresis loop, and (g) low hysteresis loss. The materials used are most often either mild or silicon steel, and various nickel−iron alloys sometimes with the addition of copper and/or cobalt, but iron/cobalt alloys are also used. Some of these alloys have commercial names, e.g., mumetal is an alloy of iron, copper, manganese and nickel, and radiometal is a 50% nickel−iron alloy.

Ferrites are a class of non-metallic magnetic materials that have both a high permeability and a high resistivity. The latter is useful when a material will be subjected to repeated cycles of magnetization when eddy currents (p. 61) could become a problem.

The ferrite material consists of a compound of iron oxide, nickel and zinc particles that are held together by a binding agent and then formed by a high-temperature process. Other ferrites employ manganese−zinc particles.

4 Electromagnetism

This chapter gives a simple introduction to the fundamental principles of, and the laws governing, electromagnetic induction. Whenever a current flows in a conductor a magnetic field is set up around that conductor the direction of which can always be determined by the use of the corkscrew rule. If the conductor is situated within a magnetic field the two magnetic fields will combine and the resultant field will exert a force upon the conductor. This effect is known as the *motor principle*, since a motor is a machine that converts input electrical energy into output mechanical energy.

Whenever there is a relative motion between a conductor and a magnetic field an e.m.f. will be induced into the conductor. This is often known as the *generator effect* since a generator is a machine that converts mechanical energy into electrical energy. The relative motion may occur because the conductor is moved through a stationary magnetic field, or because the conductor is in a fixed position and the field is varied, or because both the conductor and the field are in motion. Faraday's law of electromagnetic induction states that the magnitude of the induced e.m.f. is directly proportional to the rate of change of flux linkages, $d\Phi/dt$*. Lenz's law of electromagnetic induction states that the direction of the e.m.f. induced into a conductor moving in a magnetic field is always such as to oppose the change producing the e.m.f.

The magnetic field set up by the current flowing in a conductor will induce an e.m.f. into that conductor if the current, and hence the magnetic flux, should change. This effect is known as *self inductance*. An e.m.f. will also be induced into any other conductor that is in the close vicinity of the current-carrying conductor and this effect is known as *mutual inductance*. The main application of mutual inductance is in the device known as a *transformer*; this device is widely employed in all branches of electrical engineering to transform voltages from one value to another.

Electromagnetic induction

Faraday's law of electromagnetic induction states that whenever the magnetic flux that links a conductor changes, an e.m.f. will be induced into that conductor. The magnitude of the induced e.m.f. is directly proportional to the rate of change of the flux linkages. The changes in the flux linkages may take place because the conductor is moving through a stationary magnetic field (as in a generator) or because the

*The notation $d\Phi/dt$ will continually be employed throughout the remainder of this book to denote 'a change of'. Thus $d\Phi/dt$ means (change of flux)/(change of time) and dI/dt means (change of current)/(change of time).

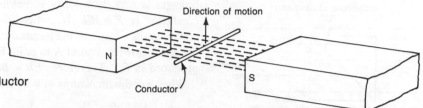

Fig. 4.1 Movement of a conductor through a magnetic field

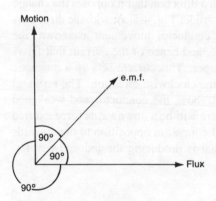

Fig. 4.2 Relative directions of induced e.m.f., flux and motion

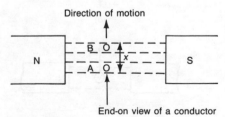

Fig. 4.3 Conductor moving in a magnetic field

magnetic field varies around a fixed conductor (as in a transformer) or sometimes because both the magnetic field and the conductor are in motion. The relative movement of the conductor to the magnetic field must have a component that is at right-angles to the direction of the field for an e.m.f. to be induced into the conductor. If the relative movement of the conductor is parallel to the direction of the field there will be zero change in the flux linkages and so zero induced e.m.f.

When a coil of wire with N turns is considered an e.m.f. will be induced into each turn and the effective flux linkages will be equal to the product of the magnetic flux and the number of turns, i.e., flux linkages = $N\Phi$. Since the flux itself is proportional to the number of turns (m.m.f. = NI) the flux linkages are proportional to the square of the number of turns, N^2.

When the flux linkages change at the rate of 1 Wb/s the induced voltage is equal to 1 volt.

Figure 4.1 shows a straight length of a conductor, which forms a part of a complete circuit, that is being moved upwards through a uniform magnetic field. As the conductor moves there is a continual change in flux linkages and an e.m.f. is induced into the conductor. The direction of the induced e.m.f. is mutually at right-angles to both the magnetic field and to the direction in which the conductor is moved. This is shown by Fig. 4.2. The e.m.f. is only induced into the part of the conductor that is actually in the magnetic field; this is known as the active part of the conductor.

The magnitude E of the induced e.m.f. is equal to the rate of change of the flux linkages, i.e.,

$$E = d\Phi/dt \quad \text{V.} \tag{4.1}$$

Figure 4.3 shows the end-on view of the conductor. The conductor moves from position A to position B with a constant velocity of v m/s and the distance x between the two points is equal to vt metres, where t is the time taken.

Therefore, $E = dBA/dt = dBlx/dt$, where l is the active length in metres of the conductor, or

$$E = Blv \quad \text{V.} \tag{4.2}$$

This expression can be obtained in two other ways: (i) The conductor moves the distance x between the points A and B in t seconds and the flux linked is $\Phi = BA = Blx$ Wb. The rate of change of flux

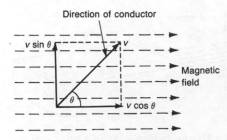

Fig. 4.4 Resolving velocity into its horizontal and vertical components

linkages is $E = Blx/t = Blv$ as before. (ii) The force acting on the conductor is $F = BlI$ N, where I is the current flowing in the conductor as a result of the induced e.m.f. The work done in moving the conductor from point A to point B is Fx and the electrical energy produced is EIt. Therefore, $EIt = BlIx$, $E = Blx/t = Blv$.

When a coil with N turns of wire is considered the induced e.m.f. is

$$E = Nd\Phi/dt \quad \text{V}. \tag{4.3}$$

Very often the conductor will not move perpendicularly to the magnetic field but at some angle θ to it. When this is the case, Fig. 4.4, the velocity v of the conductor must be resolved into two components; one component, $v \sin \theta$, is at right-angles to the field and induces an e.m.f. into the conductor, the other component, $v \cos \theta$, is parallel to the magnetic field and it does not induce any voltage into the conductor. Therefore,

$$\text{induced e.m.f. } E = Blv \sin \theta \quad \text{V} \tag{4.4}$$

Figure 4.5 shows further examples of the relative directions of the magnetic field strength, the movement of the conductor, and the induced e.m.f. The direction of the induced e.m.f. can also be deduced by the use of Lenz's law. This states that 'the direction of the induced e.m.f. is always such that any current it causes to flow will set up a magnetic flux which is in such a direction that it opposes the change that is producing the e.m.f.' Consider Fig. 4.5(a); with the directions of the magnetic field and the conductor movement as shown, the direction of the induced e.m.f., and hence of the current that flows in the conductor, is into the paper. This current sets up a magnetic field around the conductor in the clockwise direction. The resultant magnetic field is strengthened above the conductor and weakened below the conductor so that there will be a downwards force exerted upon the conductor. This is, of course, in opposition to the upwards movement of the conductor that is producing the induced e.m.f.

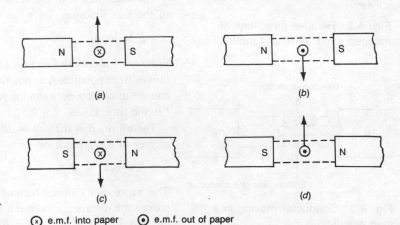

Fig. 4.5 Relative directions of magnetic field, motion of conductor and the induced e.m.f.

⊗ e.m.f. into paper   ⊙ e.m.f. out of paper

Example 4.1

A straight conductor is 3 cm long and it is moved with a constant velocity of 10 m/s perpendicularly to a uniform magnetic field. If the flux density of the magnetic field is 0.75 T calculate (a) the e.m.f. induced into the conductor, and (b) the force exerted upon the conductor if it is connected to a 10 Ω resistor.

Solution

(a) $E = Blv = 0.75 \times 0.03 \times 10 = 0.225$ V.   (Ans.)
(b) $I = 0.225/10 = 22.5$ mA.
   $F = BlI = 0.75 \times 0.03 \times 22.5 \times 10^{-3} = 506\ \mu$N.   (Ans.)

Example 4.2

A straight 10 cm length of conductor is moved at an angle of 60° to a uniform magnetic field of flux density 1 T. Calculate the velocity with which the conductor must move in order to generate an induced e.m.f. of 100 mV.

Solution

From equation (4.4), $0.1 = 1 \times 0.01 \times v \sin 60°$
   or $v = 11.55$ m/s.   (Ans.)

Rectangular coil

Suppose that the rectangular coil shown in Fig. 4.6(a) is of length l and width w and is made to rotate clockwise in the magnetic field with a constant angular velocity of ω rad/s. The axis of rotation is perpendicular to the magnetic field. Each end of the coil is connected to a *slip-ring* and electrical contact to these slip-rings is made by graphite brushes. Figure 4.6(b) shows an end view of the coil rotating about the axis OO. The instantaneous velocity of the coil's sides that are parallel to the axis is tangential to the circle described by the coil radius $w/2$. The peripheral velocity is constant at v m/s, where $v = \omega$ times radius of coil $= \omega w/2$ and it is represented by the phasor v.

The phasor v has a component $v \cos \theta$ parallel to the magnetic field, and another component $v \sin \theta$ perpendicular to the field. Phasor $v \cos \theta$ represents the component of the peripheral velocity parallel to the magnetic field and the motion represented by this component experiences zero changes in flux linkages and so it does not induce an e.m.f. into the coil. Component $v \sin \theta$ is at right-angles to the magnetic field and so it does experience changes in flux linkages as the coil rotates. An e.m.f. is hence generated, the magnitude of which is given by

$$E = BNlv \sin \theta \quad \text{V} \tag{4.5}$$

This e.m.f. will be generated by both sides of the coil and so the total instantaneous e.m.f. is

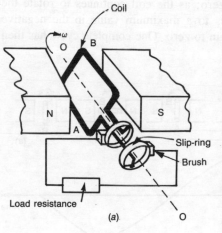

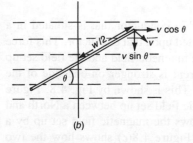

Fig. 4.6 Rectangular coil in a magnetic field

$$2E = 2BNlv \sin \theta = 2BNl\omega(w/2) \sin \theta$$
$$= BNlw\omega \sin \theta. \tag{4.6}$$
$$= BNA\omega \sin \theta \quad \text{V.} \tag{4.7}$$

where A is the area of the coil.

Example 4.3

A rectangular coil has the dimensions $l = 0.05$ m, $w = 0.02$ m and has 500 turns. The coil rotates at an angular velocity of 5000 rad/s in a uniform magnetic field of 0.06 T. Calculate the induced e.m.f.

Solution
From equation (4.6),
$$E = 0.06 \times 0.05 \times 0.02 \times 500 \times 5000 = 150 \text{ V.} \quad (Ans.)$$

Figure 4.7 shows the induced voltage for five consecutive quarter-rotations of the coil assuming that the voltage is positive when the B side of the coil is rising. As the coil rotates the generated e.m.f. increases from zero to its maximum positive value V_m as θ changes from 0° to +90°. As θ changes from +90° to 180° the generated voltage falls from V_m to zero; as the coil continues to rotate the generated voltage increases to a maximum value in the negative direction and then falls again to zero. One complete cycle has then been completed.

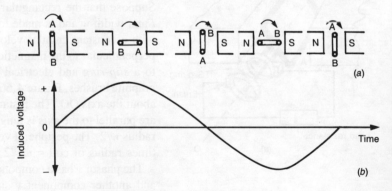

Fig. 4.7 Showing the induced e.m.f. for five consecutive quarter-rotations of coil

The motor principle

When a current is passed through a conductor that is situated in a magnetic field a force will be exerted upon that conductor. This force arises because the resultant of the magnetic field and the field set up around the conductor by the current is stronger on one side of the conductor than on the other side. This is shown by Fig. 4.8. Figure 4.8(a) shows the uniform magnetic field set up between a North and a South pole and Fig. 4.8(b) shows the magnetic field set up by a current flowing in a conductor. Figure 4.8(c) shows how the two magnetic fields combine to give a resultant field in which the lines of flux are in the same direction above the conductor and in opposite

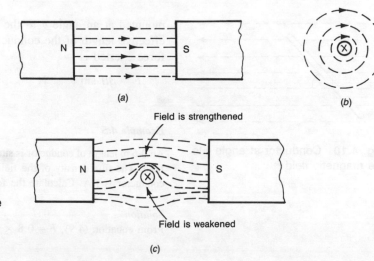

Fig. 4.8 (c) Shows the effect on the magnetic field in (a) when the current-carrying conductor in (b) is placed in the field

Field is strengthened

Field is weakened

(a)

(b)

(c)

directions underneath the conductor. Since the flux lines always try to shorten their length there is a downwards force exerted upon the conductor. If the direction of the current flowing in the conductor is reversed the force will be exerted in the upwards direction instead.

The magnitude of the force is proportional to the flux density B, to the current I, and to the length of the conductor in the magnetic field, i.e.,

$$F = BlI \quad \text{N.} \tag{4.8}$$

Example 4.4

A conductor in a uniform magnetic field of flux density 0.5 T has an active length of 0.4 m and carries a current of 1 A. Calculate the force exerted upon the conductor.

Solution
$F = BlI = 0.5 \times 0.4 \times 1 = 0.2 \,\text{N}.$ (*Ans.*)

The directions of the magnetic field, the current, and the force exerted upon the conductor are mutually at right-angles as shown by Fig. 4.9. (Figure 4.9(a) relates to Fig. 4.8(c).) If the conductor is

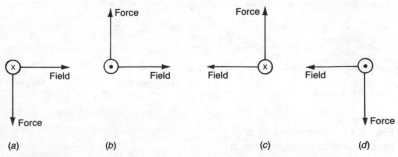

Fig. 4.9 Relative directions of the magnetic field, the current and the force exerted on the conductor

Force

Field

Force

(a)

Force

Field

(b)

Force

Field

(c)

Force

Field

Force

(d)

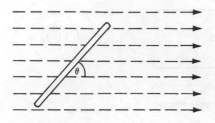

Fig. 4.10 Conductor at angle θ to the magnetic field

mounted at an angle θ to the magnetic field, as in Fig. 4.10, the effective length of the conductor inside the field is $l \sin \theta$ and the force exerted is

$$F = BlI \sin \theta \qquad \text{N} \tag{4.9}$$

Example 4.5

An 0.6 m length of conductor is situated in, and at 45° to, a uniform magnetic field. The flux density of the field is 0.8 T and the current flowing in the conductor is 1 A. Calculate the force exerted on the conductor.

Solution
From equation (4.9), $F = 0.8 \times 0.6 \times 1 \times \sin 45° = 0.34$ N.   (*Ans.*)

Coil in a magnetic field

Figure 4.11(*a*) shows a coil with N turns that is wound upon a rectangular former l metres long and w metres wide and is mounted so that it is able to rotate about an axis. The coil is situated within a uniform magnetic field of flux density B tesla and at an angle θ to the field. The end view of the coil is shown in Fig. 4.11(*b*). The forces exerted on the sides of the coil will always be perpendicular to the field but the forces exerted upon the short sides are in opposite directions to one another and so they cancel out. It is only the two long sides of the coil that have an effective force exerted upon them. As shown in the figure the force on each of the long conductors can be resolved into two forces that are mutually at right-angles. The component $F \sin \theta$ will be radial, i.e., through the axis of rotation

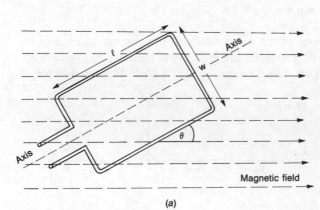

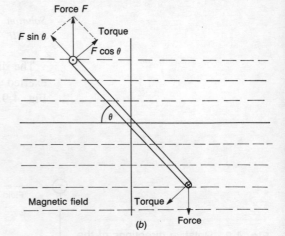

Fig. 4.11 Two views of a rectangular coil mounted in a magnetic field

of the coil, and so it will exert zero torque on the coil. The component $F \cos \theta$ is at right-angles to the radius and hence this component of the force does exert a torque on the coil. This is true for each of the long conductors and they are therefore both subjected to a torque.

The force F exerted upon each of the long conductors is $F = BlI$ N. The torque applied to each of these conductors is equal to $Fr \cos \theta$, where θ is the angle between the coil and the magnetic field and r is the radius of the coil $= w/2$. Since there are N turns the total torque T applied to the coil is

$$T = 2NFr \cos \theta \quad \text{Nm.} \tag{4.10}$$

The maximum torque is applied to the coil when the plane of the coil is parallel to the magnetic field, then $\theta = 0$ and $\cos \theta = 1$.

Example 4.6

Calculate the force on a coil of 200 turns that carries a current of 2 A in a magnetic field of flux density 0.2 T. The dimensions of the coil are: length $= 0.2$ m, width $= 0.1$ m.

Solution
$$F = BlI = 0.2 \times 0.2 \times 2 \times 200 \times 2 = 32 \text{ N.} \quad (Ans.)$$

Example 4.7

A rectangular coil has long sides of length 10 cm and short sides of length 5 cm and 60 turns of wire. The coil is mounted at angle of 45° to a uniform magnetic field of flux density 0.6 T. Calculate the torque applied to the coil when a current of 0.25 A flows through the windings.

Solution
$$T = 2NFr \cos \theta = 2(0.6 \times 0.25 \times 0.01) \times 0.025 \times 0.707 \times 60$$
$$= 3.18 \times 10^{-3} \text{ Nm.} \quad (Ans.)$$

If a square-shaped coil is placed in a radial magnetic field, see Fig. 4.12(a), the long sides of the coil will always move at right-angles to the field, Fig. 4.12(b). The force on each side of the coil is now $F = NBIl$ N and the torque exerted is $2NBIlr$ Nm.

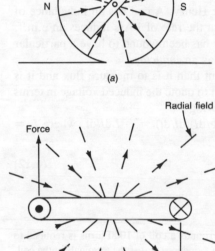

(a)

Radial field

Force

Force

(b)

Fig. 4.12 Use of a radial magnetic field

Self-inductance

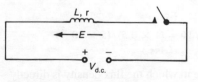

L, r

$\leftarrow E \rightarrow$

$+ \quad -$
$V_{d.c.}$

Fig. 4.13 Coil suddenly applied to a d.c. voltage

When a current flows in a conductor a magnetic field is set up that links with that conductor. If the current should change for any reason the flux will also change and the change in flux linkages will induce an e.m.f. into the conductor. This is known as Faraday's law of induction. The property of the conductor whereby this *back e.m.f.* can be induced into it is known as the *self-inductance*, or just the *inductance*, of the conductor. The magnitude of the induced e.m.f. is equal to the rate of change of flux linkages, i.e., $E = d\Phi/dt$.

If a coil is suddenly applied to a d.c. voltage source, see Fig. 4.13, a current will start to flow in the coil. The current will not instantaneously increase from zero to the value predicted by Ohm's law, i.e., $I = V/R$ where R is the sum of the internal resistance of the supply and the winding resistance of the coil. Immediately a current commences to flow a magnetic field is set up around the conductor and as the current starts to increase so must the magnetic flux. The changing flux will link with the turns of the coil and induce an e.m.f. into each of the windings. The direction of this back e.m.f. is, from Lenz's law, such that it opposes the force creating it. The polarity of the back e.m.f. is hence opposite to the polarity of the applied voltage source and this is shown by Fig. 4.12. The magnitude of the back e.m.f. is equal to the number of turns in the coil times the rate of change of flux linkages, i.e.,

$$E = -N\mathrm{d}\Phi/\mathrm{d}t \quad \text{V.} \tag{4.11}$$

The unit of inductance is the Henry. A coil has an inductance of 1 henry if a current changing at the rate of 1 A/s induces an e.m.f. of 1 V into the coil. A coil that has been wound to have a particular value of inductance is known as an *inductor*.

It is easier to measure current than it is to measure flux and it is therefore often more convenient to quote the induced voltage in terms of a change in the current flowing.
$E = -(N\mathrm{d}\Phi/\mathrm{d}t) = -(N\mathrm{d}\Phi/\mathrm{d}I)(\mathrm{d}I/\mathrm{d}t) = -L\mathrm{d}I/\mathrm{d}t$, where $L = N\mathrm{d}\Phi/\mathrm{d}I$. Therefore,

$$E = -L\mathrm{d}I/\mathrm{d}t \quad \text{V.} \tag{4.12}$$

Example 4.8

A steady flux of 500 μWb that surrounds a coil of 1000 turns is reduced to 125 μWb in 1 ms. Calculate the e.m.f. induced across the terminals of the coil.

Solution

Change of flux $\mathrm{d}\Phi = 500 - 125 = 375 \ \mu$Wb.
Induced e.m.f. $= -1000 \times (375 \times 10^{-6})/(1 \times 10^{-3})$
$\qquad\qquad\qquad = -375$ V. (*Ans.*)

Example 4.9

When the current flowing in a 1 H inductor varies by 0.5 A the flux produced changes by 5 mWb. Calculate the number of turns in the inductor.

Solution

$E = N\mathrm{d}\Phi/\mathrm{d}t = L\mathrm{d}I/\mathrm{d}t, \ N = L\mathrm{d}I/\mathrm{d}\Phi = (1 \times 0.5)/(5 \times 10^{-3})$
$\qquad\qquad\qquad\qquad = 100.$ (*Ans.*)

If a coil or an inductor has a core in which the flux density is directly proportional to the current flowing in the windings, i.e., an air core, the inductance L is equal to the number of flux linkages per ampere of current. Thus,

$$L = N\Phi/I \quad \text{H} \tag{4.13}$$

Example 4.10

A 50 mH coil carrying a current of 0.5 A produces a flux of 50 Wb. Calculate the number of turns in the coil.

Solution

From equation (4.13), $N = LI/\Phi = (50 \times 10^{-3} \times 0.5)/(50 \times 10^{-6})$
$= 500.$ (Ans.)

Relationship between inductance and reluctance

From equation (4.13),

$$L = N\Phi/I = NBA/I = N\mu HA/I = N\mu NIA/Il$$
$$= \mu N^2 A/l = N^2/(l/\mu A),$$
$$\text{or} \quad L = N^2/S \quad \text{H.} \quad (Ans.)$$

This means that an air-cored inductor has an inductance that is directly proportional to both (a) the square of the number of turns, (b) the cross-sectional area of the core. The inductance is inversely proportional to the length of the core.

If the inductor has an iron core the relative permeability μ_r of the core material will greatly increase its inductance. Since the relative permeability of any magnetic material is *not* constant the inductance will vary with the current flowing in the windings. However, provided the component is operated over the linear part of the magnetization curve the inductance value is fairly constant.

Example 4.11

A coil of 300 turns is wound on an iron core of length 5 cm and cross-sectional area 2 cm². A current of 100 mA flows in the coil. Calculate (a) the flux set up in the core , and (b) the inductance of the coil. The core material has the data given in Table 4.1.

Solution

(a) $H = NI/l = (300 \times 0.1)/(5 \times 10^{-2}) = 600$ A/m.
From the given data $B = 1.2$ T.
$\Phi = BA = 1.2 \times 2 \times 10^{-4} = 2.4 \times 10^{-4}$ Wb.   (Ans.)
(b) $L = N\Phi/I = (300 \times 2.4 \times 10^{-4})/0.1 = 0.72$ H.   (Ans.)

Table 4.1

Magnetic field strength H (A/m)	200	600	700	1000	2000	3500
Flux density B (T)		1	1.2	1.3	1.4	1.5	1.6

Mutual inductance

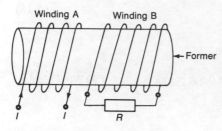

Fig. 4.14 Mutual inductance

Two conductors, or two coils or inductors, are said to possess *mutual inductance* if a change in the current flowing in one of the conductors, or inductors, induces an e.m.f. into the other conductor or inductor. When a current I flows in winding A in Fig. 4.14 a magnetic field is set up in the core and this flux links with the turns of both windings. An e.m.f. is therefore induced into both of the windings; the e.m.f. induced into winding A is, of course, the self-induced e.m.f. that has already been discussed. The e.m.f. induced into winding B is due to the change of mutual flux linkages. If winding B has its terminals connected to a resistor as shown a current will flow in this winding. The direction of the mutually induced e.m.f. will always be such that the flux produced by the current flowing in winding B will oppose the flux set up by the current in winding A. When the current flowing in winding A is switched off the flux produced by it will decrease and this change in the flux linkages will cause the e.m.f. induced into winding B to reverse its polarity. The current in winding B will then flow in the opposite direction to before and the flux that it sets up in the core will oppose the fall in the flux due to winding A and so tend to maintain it. The flux set up by the current flowing in winding B will also induce an e.m.f. into winding B itself so that both windings possess self inductance. The two windings are said to be *inductively coupled* together.

If the former upon which the two coils are wound has an iron core the flux will be concentrated in the core and most of the flux set up by the current in one winding will link with the turns of the other winding. This is the case in a *transformer* used at low frequencies. If, however, an air core is used only a small fraction of the flux produced by one winding will link with the turns of the other winding. This fraction is generally known as the *coupling coefficient k*.

Let the flux set up in the core by a current I_A flowing in winding A be Φ. Then the effective flux that links with winding B is $k\Phi$ and the e.m.f. induced into winding B is

$$-N_B k\,d\Phi/dt = -(N_B k\,d\Phi/dI_A)(dI_A/dt),$$

or $\qquad E = -M\,dI_A/dt \qquad$ V $\qquad\qquad$ (4.14)

where the *mutual inductance*

$$M = N_B k\,d\Phi/dI_A. \qquad\qquad (4.15)$$

Two coils have a mutual inductance of 1 henry if an e.m.f. of 1 V is induced into one of the coils when the current in the other coil changes at the rate of 1 A/s.

Example 4.12

The two inductors shown in Fig. 4.15 have a mutual inductance of 0.05 H. If the current in the 0.2 H inductor increases at a uniform rate from 0.2 to 2 A in 4 ms calculate the e.m.f. induced into the 0.3 H inductor.

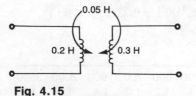

Fig. 4.15

Solution

$$E = -M dI_A/dt = -0.05 \times (2 - 0.2)/(4 \times 10^{-3})$$
$$= 22.5 \text{ V}. \quad (Ans.)$$

Relationship between mutual inductance and self-inductance

From equation (4.13), $L_A = N_A d\Phi/dI_A$ and $L_B = N_B d\Phi/dI_B$. From equation (4.14),

$$M = kN_B d\Phi/dI_A.$$

Hence,

$$d\Phi/dI_A = L_A/N_A$$

and so

$$M = kN_B L_A/N_A. \tag{4.16}$$

Similarly,

$$M = kN_A L_B/N_B. \tag{4.17}$$

Multiplying equations (4.16) and (4.17) together gives

$$M^2 = k^2 L_A L_B$$

or $\quad M = k\sqrt{(L_A L_B)} \quad$ H $\tag{4.18}$

Example 4.13

Two inductors have respective self inductances of 20 mH and 50 mH and a mutual inductance of 1 mH. Calculate the value of the coupling coefficient k.

Solution
From equation (4.18), $k = 1/\sqrt{(20 \times 50)} = 0.032$. $\quad (Ans.)$

Example 4.14

Two coils having 1000 turns and 2000 turns respectively are wound on a common iron core of mean length 250 cm and cross-sectional area 20 cm^2. The relative permeability of the iron is 600 and the coupling coefficient between the two coils is 0.85. Calculate (a) the self-inductance of each coil, and (b) their mutual inductance.

Solution
(a) Reluctance $S = l/\mu_0 \mu_r A = (250 \times 10^{-2})/(4\pi \times 10^{-7} \times 600 \times 20 \times 10^{-4}) = 1.658 \times 10^6$ H^{-1}.
$L_1 = N_1^2/S = 1000^2/(1.658 \times 10^6) = 603$ mH. $\quad (Ans.)$
$L_2 = 4 \times L_1 = 2.41$ H. $\quad (Ans.)$
(b) $M = 0.85 \sqrt{(0.603 \times 2.41)} = 1.03$ H. $\quad (Ans.)$

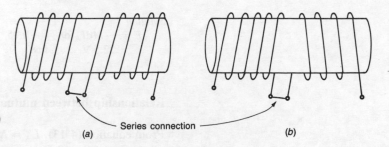

Fig. 4.16 Inductors connected in (a) series-aiding and (b) series-opposing

Series connection

(a)   (b)

Inductors in series

When two inductors are connected in series with one another they may either be connected in series-aiding or in series-opposing. The meanings of these two terms are illustrated by Figs 4.16(a) and (b). In (a) the two coils are wound in the same direction on the common former and when they are connected in series the fluxes set up in the core by each inductor are in the same direction. Hence the fluxes are additive. The mutually induced e.m.f. in each inductor is in the same direction as the self-induced e.m.f. in that inductor and so the total inductance L_T is

$$L_T = L_A + L_B + 2M \qquad (4.19)$$

In (b) the two coils are wound in opposite directions on the common former and so the fluxes set up in the core are in opposite directions. The total inductance L_T is

$$L_T = L_A + L_B - 2M \qquad (4.20)$$

Example 4.15

Two inductors of 50 mH and 150 mH respectively are wound on a common former and have a mutual inductance of 20 mH. Calculate the total inductance when the inductors are connected in (a) series-aiding, and (b) series-opposing.

Solution

(a) $L_T = 50 + 150 + 20 = 220$ mH.   (*Ans.*)
(b) $L_T = 50 + 150 - 20 = 180$ mH.   (*Ans.*)

Energy stored in an inductance

When there is zero current flowing in an inductance there is no magnetic field set up around it. If a current is then caused to flow that increases with increase in time an increasing magnetic field will be produced. Some energy must be supplied to set up this field. If the current increases at a constant rate from zero to I amps in t seconds the average value of the current will be $I/2$. The back e.m.f. induced into the inductance is $-L dI/dt = -LI/t$ volts. The applied voltage must therefore be equal to LI/t volts. The average power taken by the magnetic field is then $I/2 \times LI/t = I^2 L/2t$ watts. The total energy

E absorbed by the magnetic field is equal to the product of the power times time, or

$$\text{energy stored } E = I^2L/2 \quad \text{J.} \tag{4.21}$$

Energy is only supplied to the magnetic field when the current is increasing. This is the energy that is used in setting up the magnetic field and it is all returned to the circuit when the current is turned off. In practice, all inductors have some self-resistance and so whenever a current flows in the windings some energy will be dissipated in the form of heat.

Example 4.16

A 2 H inductor carrying a current of 4 A produces a flux of 10 mWb. Calculate (a) the number of turns on the coil, and (b) the energy stored in the magnetic field.

Solution

(a) $N = LI/\Phi = 2 \times 4/(10 \times 10^{-3}) = 800.$ (*Ans.*)
(b) $E = 4^2 \times 2 \times 0.5 = 16\,\text{J}.$ (*Ans.*)

Eddy currents

Whenever the current flowing in a coil wound on an iron core changes the flux linking the core will also change. The width dimension of the core is at right-angles to the changing flux linkages and so a changing e.m.f. will be induced across the width of the core, see Fig. 4.17(*a*). The induced e.m.f. causes an *eddy current* to flow in the core and this will produce I^2R power losses. This power loss is dissipated as heat in the core and it is known as the *eddy current loss*. To reduce the eddy current loss the iron cores of low-frequency inductors and transformers are always laminated in longitudinal planes parallel to the magnetic flux. The self-induced e.m.f. in the iron core will then be applied across a number of laminations and so there will not be a continuous path through the core in which the eddy current can flow. This is shown by Fig. 4.17(*b*). The eddy currents are restricted to the thin sections of the individual laminations across which

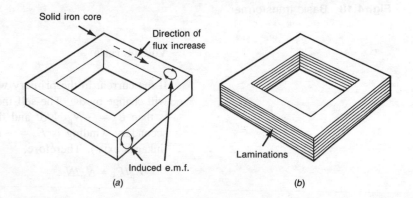

Fig. 4.17 (*a*) Production of eddy currents in a solid core, (*b*) use of laminations

Solid iron core

Direction of flux increase

Induced e.m.f.

(*a*)

Laminations

(*b*)

the induced e.m.f. is very small. The size of the eddy currents can be further minimized by the use of a high-resistivity material for the core.

The laminated core consists of a stack of a number of stampings of a magnetic material each of which is insulated by being coated with a layer of varnish so that there is a high electrical resistance between adjacent stampings. A laminated core is designed so that the changing flux is along the plane of the laminations; this ensures that the induced e.m.f. will be perpendicular to the laminations as shown in the figure.

The higher the frequency of the flux changes the thinner must be the laminations in order to keep the eddy current loss small. Eventually, the required thinness becomes impractical and either a dust core or a ferrite core has to be employed.

The transformer

A transformer consists of two coils, known as the primary winding and the secondary winding, that are wound on a common iron core that is in the shape of a closed ring or rectangle. A simple transformer is shown in Fig. 4.18. When a changing current flows in the primary winding a changing flux is set up in the iron core. This alternating flux links with every turn in the secondary winding and induces an e.m.f. into each of its turns. It also links with each turn in the primary winding and induces an e.m.f. into each of its turns. The magnitude of the total induced e.m.f. in both of the windings is equal to the change in the flux linkages, mutual or self, times the number of turns in the winding.

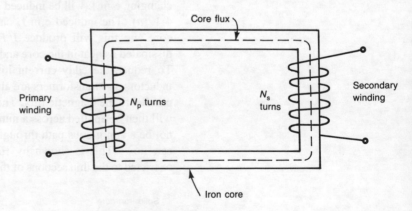

Fig. 4.18 Basic transformer

Voltage ratio

If the current in the primary winding changes by dI_p the core flux will change by $d\Phi$. The self-induced e.m.f. in the primary winding is then $E_p = -N_p d\Phi/dt$ and the mutually induced e.m.f. into the secondary winding is $E_s = -N_s d\Phi/dt$, (assuming that 100% flux linkages exist). Therefore,

$$E_p/E_s = N_p/N_s. \tag{4.22}$$

If the voltage induced into the secondary winding is greater than the voltage induced into the primary winding then $N_s > N_p$ and the transformer is known as a *step-up transformer*. Conversely, if the secondary voltage is less than the primary voltage it is a *step-down transformer*.

Current ratio

If the power losses in the transformer are assumed to be negligibly small so the output power is equal to the input power then

$$I_p E_p = I_s E_s \quad \text{and} \quad I_p/I_s = E_s/E_p = N_s/N_p \qquad (4.23)$$

This means that a transformer with a step-up voltage ratio has a step-down current ratio.

Resistance ratio

The primary current I_p is equal to V_p/R_p where R_p is the resistance of the primary circuit. Also the secondary current $I_s = V_s/R_s$. Therefore, $I_s/I_p = (V_s/R_s)/(V_p/R_p) = V_s R_p/V_p R_s$. But $V_s/V_p = N_s/N_p$, and so $I_s/I_p = N_s R_p/N_p R_s$. Hence,

$$R_p/R_s = (N_p/N_s)^2 \qquad (4.24)$$

This means that the resistance ratio of a transformer is equal to the square of the turns ratio.

Efficiency

The power output of a transformer is always smaller than the input power because of unavoidable power losses within the transformer. These losses are $I^2 R$ (copper losses) in the resistance of the windings, and eddy current and hysteresis losses (iron losses) in the core.

The efficiency η of a transformer is

$$\eta = (\text{output power})/(\text{input power}) \times 100\% \qquad (4.25)$$

The efficiency is always less than 100% because of the copper and iron losses.

Example 4.17

An ideal transformer supplies a power of 400 W to a 250 Ω load when the primary winding is connected to a 240 V supply. Calculate (*a*) the voltage across the load, (*b*) the turns ratio, and (*c*) the primary current.

Solution
(a) $V_L = \sqrt{(400 \times 250)} = 316.2$ V. (*Ans.*)
(b) $n = N_s/N_p = 316.2/240 = 1.32 : 1$. (*Ans.*)
(c) $I_p = 400/240 = 1.67$ A. (*Ans.*)

Example 4.18

Determine the turns ratio of a transformer that is to be used to match a 50 Ω load to a 1000 Ω source.

Solution
The term 'match' means to make the input resistance of the transformer equal to the source resistance while, at the same time, making the output resistance of the transformer equal to the load resistance, see Fig. 4.19.
From equation (4.24), $n = \sqrt{(1000/50)} = 4.47$. (*Ans.*)

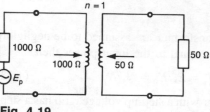

Fig. 4.19

Construction of a transformer

Essentially a transformer consists of two, and sometimes more, separate turns of wire that are wound on a common magnetic core. Even at low frequencies a solid magnetic core cannot be used because there would otherwise be considerable eddy current losses. Transformers operating at the mains frequency of 50 Hz use a laminated core to reduce the eddy current loss to an acceptable figure. The design of the core must also reduce leakage flux to the absolute minimum. There are several different core designs used for small mains transformers such as are used for the power supplies for electronic and telecommunication equipment. These are shown in Fig. 4.20. Figure 4.20(a) shows a core with two outer limbs and one centre limb; the windings are wound on a former and then the former is placed around the centre limb. The secondary winding may be wound on top of the primary winding or perhaps the primary winding may be sandwiched in between two parts of the secondary winding. It can been seen that each lamination consists of an 'E' section and an 'I' section shown separately in Figure 4.20(b). Alternatively, two 'F'

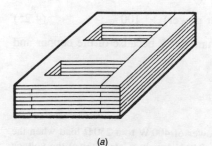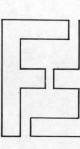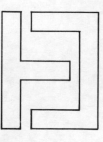

(a) (b) (c) (d)

Fig. 4.20 Transformer cores

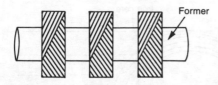

Fig. 4.21 Pie-type winding

sections, see Figure 4.20(*c*), or alternate 'U' and 'T', see Figure 4.20(*d*), sections may be employed. When an air gap is required the centre limb is made slightly shorter than shown so that it does not quite reach the other section.

The eddy current loss increases with increase in frequency and so increasingly thin laminations are required as the frequency is raised. At the lower radio frequencies laminated cores can no longer be used and ferrite cores are used instead.

At radio frequencies the self-capacitance of the windings may have a significant adverse effect and so windings must be wound in such a way as to minimize the self-capacitance. Perhaps the most commonly employed method of winding a coil to have a low self-capacitance is the 'pie-type' winding shown in Fig. 4.21. The winding(s) is/are split into three 'pies' each of which is wound so that the turns of one layer are separated by air, and the turns of adjacent layers cross one another at an angle, i.e., the winding is zig-zag.

Spark quenching

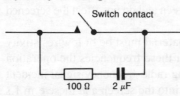

Fig. 4.22 Spark-quench circuit

When a steady current flows in an inductor the magnetic flux that is set up is also steady and there will not be any induced e.m.f. When the current is switched off a rapid change in magnetic flux will occur and so there will be a high rate of change of flux linkages. An e.m.f. is then induced into the inductor that is equal to $L\mathrm{d}I/\mathrm{d}t = N\mathrm{d}\Phi/\mathrm{d}t$.

The induced e.m.f. can very easily be of high value and it may well be sufficiently large to exceed the dielectric strength of the air; if this is so a momentary arc — a spark — will occur between the switch contacts. The spark will dissipate most of the energy that was stored in the magnetic field, the remainder of the energy being dissipated in the form of heat, i.e., I^2R losses in the resistance of the inductor. Such a spark will cause radio-frequency interference and may damage either or both the switch contacts or/and the insulation of the conductors. To avoid this possible damage occurring a *spark-quench circuit* is often fitted.

Figure 4.22 shows a simple spark-quench circuit; it can be seen to consist of a resistor and a capacitor connected in series with each other and across the switch contacts. The induced e.m.f. that appears across the contacts when the current is switched off now only produces a harmless current through the spark-quench circuit. The magnetic energy is now transferred into the electric field within the capacitor and some energy is dissipated in the resistor. At the end of the current flow the capacitor will discharge back into the circuit with further energy being dissipated in the resistor.

Magnetic screening

Screening, or shielding, a component, or a part of a circuit, from a magnetic field is achieved by placing the component, or part of a circuit, inside a screen. The screen must be made from a material having a high permeability and it acts as a magnetic shunt path. The

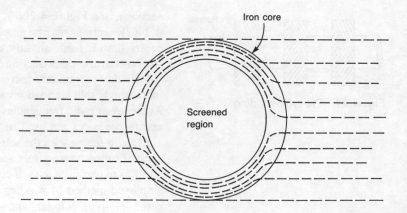

Fig. 4.23   Magnetic screening

basic principle of magnetic screening at both zero frequency and at low frequencies is shown by Fig. 4.23. The component to be protected is placed inside a circular screen that is placed within the magnetic field that the component is to be protected from. The flux lines tend to follow the low-reluctance path offered by the screen rather than the high-reluctance path inside the screen and do not affect the screened component.

At radio frequencies the screen material must be of low resistivity as well as high permeability since at these frequencies the operation of a screen is different. An interfering radio-frequency signal incident upon the screen will induce e.m.f.s into the screen and these e.m.f.s will cause eddy currents to flow in the screen. The eddy currents will set up a magnetic field whose direction is such as to oppose the interfering r.f. signal and so tend to prevent it from entering the screened region.

5 Alternating current and voltage

A current that always flows in the same direction, or a voltage that always has the same polarity, is said to be a *direct* current or voltage. The magnitude of the current, or voltage, may be constant as shown in Fig. 5.1(*a*), or it may vary with time as shown by (*b*), (*c*), (*d*), and (*e*). Figure 5.1(*a*) shows a steady direct current whose magnitude does not vary with time; such a current flows in the collector circuit of a transistor amplifier when no signal has been applied to its input terminals. Figure 5.1(*b*) shows a varying direct current; clearly the magnitude of the current is not constant but the current always flows in the same direction. This is the kind of waveform that occurs in the collector circuit of a transistor amplifier when a signal is applied to its input terminals. A *sawtooth* waveform is shown by Fig. 5.1(*c*); the magnitude of the voltage (or current) is directly proportional to time until the maximum voltage is reached and then the voltage very rapidly falls back to zero and commences another *ramp*. Such a waveform is used in the timebase circuit of a television receiver or a cathode ray oscilloscope. When a capacitor is charged from a constant voltage source the voltage across the capacitor terminals increases with increase in time in the manner shown by Fig. 5.1(*d*). When the capacitor is discharged via a resistor its terminal voltage falls towards zero rapidly at first and then more slowly as shown. Lastly, Fig. 5.1(*e*) shows a *unipolar* or single-current digital waveform that is sometimes used for the transmission of telegraphy or data information. The information is signalled by the application, and the

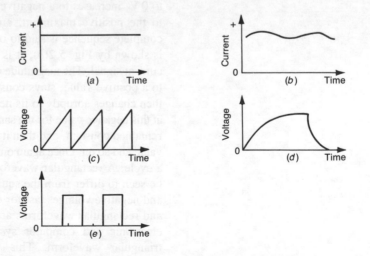

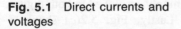

Fig. 5.1 Direct currents and voltages

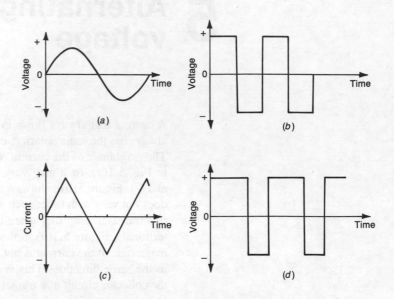

Fig. 5.2 Alternating currents and voltages

removal, of the voltage applied to the sending end of a transmission line.

An alternating current or voltage waveform is one whose direction of flow, or whose polarity, is continually changing with time. Some examples of alternating waveforms are shown in Fig. 5.2. The waveform shown in Fig. 5.2(a) is that of a sinusoidal wave and it is very important in electrical and analogue electronic engineering. The mains electricity supply to houses, offices, factories, etc., is always sinusoidal, most oscillators in electronic equipment produce sinusoidal waveforms, and the sine wave is used for routine tests and measurements on both transmission lines and analogue electronic equipment. It can be seen from the figure that the wave starts from 0 V at time $t = 0$, increases to a positive maximum, then decreases to 0 V, increases to a negative maximum that is of equal magnitude to the positive maximum, and then decreases again to 0 V. The complete sequence is said to occupy one *cycle*. A square waveform is shown by Fig. 5.2(b); it is often said to be a *bipolar* or double-current signal. The magnitude of the wave changes abruptly from 0 V to a positive value, stays constant at this value for a short time and then changes abruptly to its negative value. It then remains constant at this negative value for the same length of time as the positive voltage remained constant, and then it suddenly changes back to the positive value and so on. Once again one complete sequence of events is called a cycle. A rectangular waveform is shown in Fig. 5.2(d) and it can be seen to differ from the square waveform only in that its positive and negative voltages last for different periods of time. Both square and rectangular waveforms are commonly employed in both digital electronic and computer systems. Lastly, Fig. 5.2(c) shows a triangular waveform. This waveform, like the sinusoidal and

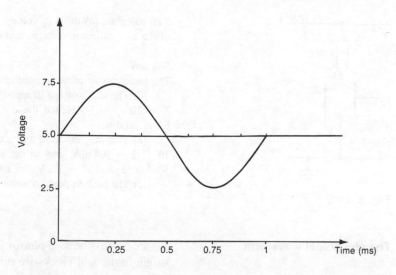

Fig. 5.3 d.c. voltage with superimposed a.c. voltage

rectangular waveforms, changes its polarity at regular intervals of time but now the change from positive to negative voltage, or from negative to positive voltage, occurs at a constant rate.

In all alternating waveforms the wave repeats its sequence of events, known as a cycle, after a time known as the periodic time or just the period.

It has become common practice to replace the words direct and alternating with the abbreviations d.c. and a.c. respectively. Thus, 'a d.c. current' means a direct current (not a direct current current) and an 'a.c. voltage' means an alternating voltage (not an alternating current voltage). This practice is followed throughout this book.

A fluctuating d.c. current, or voltage, can always be regarded as an a.c. current superimposed upon a d.c. current. Figure 5.3 shows an example; the voltage starts from $+5$ V at time $t = 0$ and rises in a sinusoidal manner to its maximum value of $+7.5$ V at time $t = 0.25$ ms. The voltage then starts to fall, again sinusoidally, passes through its mean value of $+5$ V at $t = 0.5$ ms and reaches its minimum value of $+2.5$ V at time $t = 0.75$ ms. The voltage then increases again and reaches its mean value of $+5$ V at time $t = 1$ ms. At all times the polarity of the voltage is positive and hence this is an example of a d.c. voltage. It will, however, often be more convenient to consider the wave to consist of the sum of a d.c. voltage of $+5$ V and an a.c. voltage that varies between the limits of ±2.5 V.

Example 5.1

The quiescent (steady) value of the collector current of a transistor amplifier is 2 mA. A signal applied to the base of the transistor causes the collector current to increase to a maximum of 2.4 mA and decrease to a minimum of 1.6 mA. If the collector supply voltage is 12 V and the collector resistor is

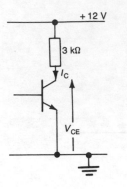

Fig. 5.4

3 kΩ calculate (*a*) the d.c. voltage V_{CE} at the collector, (*b*) the peak value of the a.c. collector voltage, and (*c*) the peak-to-peak collector voltage.

Solution
The basic circuit of the amplifier is shown by Fig. 5.4.

(*a*) The d.c. voltage dropped across the 3 kΩ resistor is $2 \times 10^{-3} \times 3 \times 10^{3} = 6$ V. Hence the d.c. collector voltage $V_{CE} = 12 - 6 = 6$ V. (*Ans.*)

(*b*) The magnitude of the a.c. collector current is $[(2.4 - 1.6) \times 10^{-3}]/2 = 0.4$ mA, and so the a.c. collector voltage is equal to $0.4 \times 10^{-3} \times 3 \times 10^{3} = 1.2$ V. (*Ans.*)

(*c*) The peak-to-peak collector voltage = $7.2 - 4.8 = 2.4$ V. (*Ans.*)

The sinusoidal waveform

Figure 5.5(*a*) shows a *phasor* of length V_m that is rotating about its origin in the anti-clockwise direction with an angular velocity of ω radians per second. Initially, at time $t = 0$, the phasor is in the horizontal position pointing to the right and so it has zero vertical component. After a time t_1 seconds the phasor will have rotated through an angle of $\theta_1 = \omega t_1$ radians (or $\theta_1 \times 180/2\pi°$) as shown by Fig. 5.5(*b*). The phasor can now be resolved into two components; one component $V_m \sin \theta_1$ is in the vertical direction and the other component $V_m \cos \theta_1$ is in the horizontal direction, Fig. 5.5(*c*). The vertical component represents the *instantaneous value v* of the voltage. After time t_2 seconds the phasor will have rotated to a new position making angle θ_2 to the starting point, see Fig. 5.5(*c*). Now, therefore, the instantaneous value of the voltage is $v = V_m \sin \theta_2 = V_m \sin \omega t_2$. The phasor continues to rotate and after

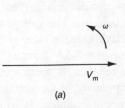

(*a*)

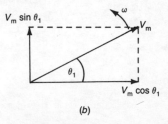

(*b*)

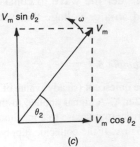

(*c*)

Fig. 5.5 Rotating phasor that generates a sinusoidal wave

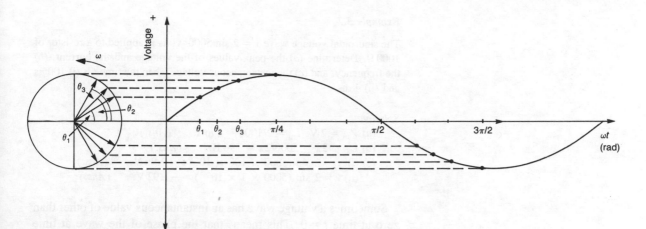

Fig. 5.6 Derivation of sinusoidal waveform

*Note: since there are 2π radians or $360°$ in a circle, to convert from (a) radians to degrees multiply by $180/\pi$, and (b) from degrees to radians multiply by $\pi/180$.

T seconds, where T is the periodic time, has rotated through 2π radians or $360°$ to describe a circle*.

The instantaneous values of the voltage for the various angles θ can be plotted against angular velocity ωt to derive the sinusoidal waveform. The method employed is shown by Fig. 5.6. The instantaneous values of voltage at each chosen angle are projected horizontally across to the time axis and points are plotted where these intersect with the vertical projections from the corresponding angles on the ωt scale. In the figure the chosen values of the angle θ are $45°$, $60°$, $90°$, $120°$, $135°$, $180°$, $225°$, $240°$, $270°$, $300°$, $325°$ and $360°$. When the phasor has rotated through one cycle and has returned to its starting point giving one cycle of the sinusoidal waveform it will carry on rotating to produce further cycles. The horizontal axis can alternatively be labelled in terms of the periodic time with $T/4 = \pi/2 = 90°$, $T/2 = 180°$, $3T/4 = 270°$ and $T = 360°$.

The instantaneous voltage of a sinusoidal wave can be algebraically represented by the equation

$$v = V_m \sin \theta = V_m \sin \omega t \quad \text{V.} \tag{5.1}$$

In this equation V_m is the *peak value* or the *amplitude* of the wave, and ω is the *angular frequency*. The *frequency f* of the wave is the number of cycles of the sine wave that are completed in every second. The unit of frequency is the Hertz (Hz). In travelling through f cycles in one second the phasor moves through $2\pi \times f$ radians per second and so

$$\omega = 2\pi f \quad \text{rad/s.} \tag{5.2}$$

The periodic time T is the time taken for the wave to go through one complete cycle and hence the periodic time is the reciprocal of the frequency of the wave, i.e.,

$$T = 1/f \quad \text{s.} \tag{5.3}$$

Example 5.2

The sinusoidal voltage wave $v = 2 \sin 5000t$ volts is applied to a resistor of $1000\,\Omega$. Determine (*a*) the peak values of the voltage and the current, (*b*) the frequency, and (*c*) the instantaneous voltage when the time t is (i) $100\,\mu s$ and (ii) 1 ms.

Solution

    (*a*) $V_m = 2\,\text{V}$. $I_m = 2/1000 = 2\,\text{mA}$.   (*Ans.*)
    (*b*) $f = \omega/2\pi = 5000/2\pi = 796\,\text{Hz}$.   (*Ans.*)
    (*c*) (i) $v = 2 \sin (5000 \times 100 \times 10^{-6}) = 0.96\,\text{V}$.   (*Ans.*)
        (ii) $v = 2 \sin (5000 \times 1 \times 10^{-3}) = -1.92\,\text{V}$.   (*Ans.*)

Sometimes a voltage wave has an instantaneous value of other than zero at time $t = 0$. This means that the phase of the wave at time $t = 0$ is $\phi°$ as shown by Fig. 5.7. The initial voltage is hence $v = V_m \sin \phi$. As the phasor rotates in the anti-clockwise direction an angular distance ωt, the total angle that the phasor makes to the reference direction is $\omega t + \phi$. Therefore, the expression representing the instantaneous value of the voltage is

$$v = V_m \sin (\omega t + \phi) \quad \text{V}. \tag{5.4}$$

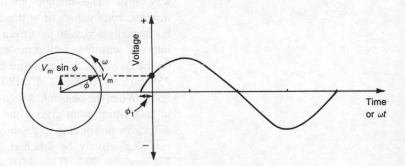

Fig. 5.7 Sine wave with non-zero voltage at time $t = 0$

Example 5.3

A sinusoidal voltage has a peak value of 10 V and a frequency of 3 MHz. If the wave has a phase angle of $30°$ at time $t = 0$ calculate the instantaneous voltage after 100 ns.

Solution

Working in radians, $30° = (30 \times 2\pi)/360 = \pi/6$ rad,
$v = 10 \sin (2\pi \times 3 \times 10^6 \times 100 \times 10^{-9} + \pi/6) = 10 \sin 2.41 = 6.69\,\text{V}$.
                                                     (*Ans.*)

Working in degrees, $(2\pi \times 300 \times 10^{-3}) \times 180/\pi = 108°$,
$v = 10 \sin (108° + 30°) = 10 \sin 138° = 6.69\,\text{V}$.   (*Ans.*)

Phase difference

When two currents at the same frequency flow in the same resistor there will, in general, be a phase difference between them and also

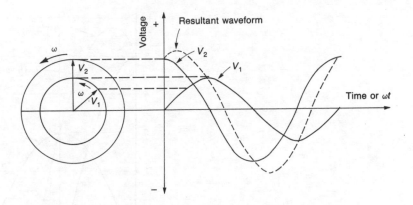

Fig. 5.8 Phase difference

between the two voltages each current develops. Figure 5.8 shows the sinusoidal waveforms plotted from two rotating phasors V_1 and V_2. Phasor V_1 starts from the horizontal at time $t = 0$ and has an initial instantaneous value of zero. The other phasor V_2 has an initial phase angle of ϕ and has an initial instantaneous voltage of $v_2 = V_2 \sin \phi$. It can be seen that the *phase difference* between the two sine waves V_1 and V_2 remains constant at ϕ. If, as is usual, the wave that has zero voltage at time $t = 0$ is taken as the reference then the voltage v_2 *leads* the voltage v_1 by the angle ϕ. It would also be correct, however, to say that the voltage v_1 lags v_2 by the same angle.

The resultant voltage waveform can be obtained by adding the instantaneous voltages of the two waveforms and the result of so doing is shown by the dotted line.

Example 5.4

Two currents, $i_1 = 3 \sin \omega t$ and $i_2 = 5 \sin (\omega t + \pi/2)$ mA flow in the same resistor of 1 kΩ. Plot one cycle of each of the current waveforms on the same axes and then draw the waveform of the resultant current. From the waveforms determine (*a*) the maximum value of the resultant current, (*b*) the phase angle between the resultant current and i_1, and (*c*) the maximum voltage across the resistor.

Solution

The data needed to draw the waveforms reasonably accurately is tabulated in Table 5.1. The required waveforms are given in Fig. 5.9. From the figure,

(*a*) Maximum current = 5.83 mA.   (*Ans.*)

Table 5.1

ωt	$\pi/6$	$\pi/3$	$\pi/2$	$2\pi/3$	$5\pi/6$	π	$7\pi/6$	$4\pi/3$	$3\pi/2$	$5\pi/3$	$11\pi/6$	2π
$\sin \omega t$	0.5	0.866	1	0.866	0.5	0	−0.5	−0.866	−1	−0.866	−0.5	0
$3 \sin \omega t$	1.5	2.6	3	2.6	1.5	0	−1.5	−2.6	−3	−2.6	−1.5	0
$\omega t + \pi/2$	$2\pi/3$	$5\pi/6$	π	$7\pi/6$	$4\pi/3$	$3\pi/2$	$5\pi/3$	$11\pi/6$	2π	$13\pi/6$	$7\pi/3$	$5\pi/2$
$\sin (\omega t + \pi/2)$	0.866	0.5	0	−0.5	−0.866	−1	−0.866	−0.5	0	0.5	0.866	1
$5 \sin (\omega t + \pi/2)$	4.33	2.5	0	−2.5	−4.33	−5	−4.33	−2.5	0	2.5	4.33	5

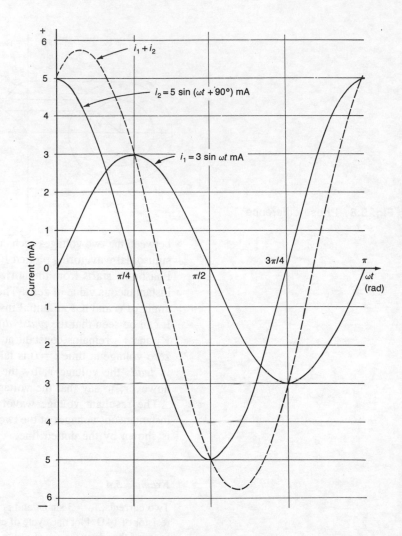

Fig. 5.9

(*b*) Phase angle between the zero points of the i_1 and resultant current waveforms is 1 radian or 57.3°.   (*Ans.*)

(*c*) Maximum voltage = $1000 \times 5.83 \times 10^{-3}$ = 5.83 V.   (*Ans.*)

Waves at different frequencies

Very often, particularly in electronic and communication engineering, a.c. signals are employed which contain components at more than one frequency. The lowest frequency in the wave is known as the *fundamental frequency*; all the other components are at integral multiples of the fundamental frequency and are known as *harmonics*. The second harmonic is at twice the fundamental frequency, the third harmonic is at three times the fundamental frequency and so on. Usually, but not always, the amplitude of a harmonic falls as the order of the harmonic increases.

Figure 5.10(*a*) shows a fundamental frequency component 10 sin ωt and a second harmonic component 5 sin $2\omega t$ volts that are in phase

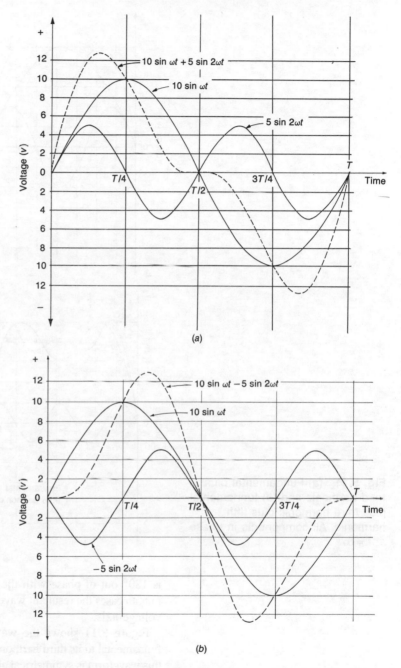

Fig. 5.10 Fundamental plus second harmonic (*a*) in phase at time $t = 0$, (*b*) 180° out of phase at time $t = 0$

with one another at time $t = 0$. Since the wave contains components at more than one frequency it is said to be a *complex wave*. The waveform of the complex signal can be obtained by adding the fundamental and the second harmonic together at a number of different points through one cycle of the fundamental. This has been done to obtain the waveform shown dotted. Figure 5.10(*b*) shows the resultant waveform of the same two components when the second harmonic

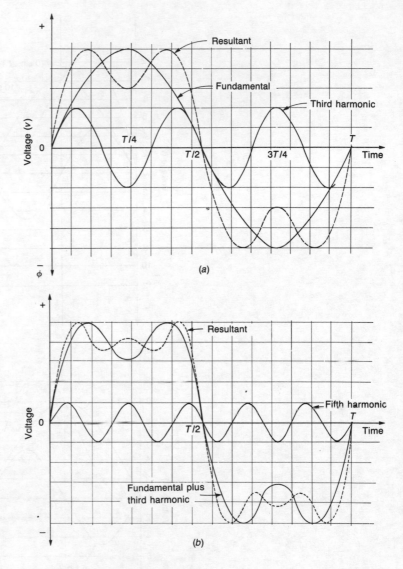

Fig. 5.11 (a) Fundamental plus third harmonic and (b) fundamental plus third harmonic plus fifth harmonic. All components in phase at $t = 0$

is 180° out of phase with the fundamental at time $t = 0$. Note that in both cases the resultant waveform is not symmetrical about the zero voltage axis.

Figure 5.11 shows the waveform that is obtained by adding a fundamental to its third harmonic that is in phase at time $t = 0$. Clearly this waveform is symmetrical about the zero voltage axis and is tending towards a rectangular shape. If the fifth harmonic, also in phase at time $t = 0$, is also added the resultant wave becomes a better approximation to a rectangular wave, see Fig. 5.11(b). Adding the seventh, the ninth, etc., *odd* harmonics produces an even better approximation to a rectangular wave.

A completely different looking waveform is obtained if the third harmonic is 180° out of phase with the fundamental at time $t = 0$ and this is shown by Fig. 5.12.

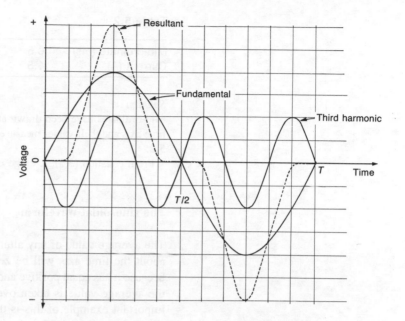

Fig. 5.12 Fundamental plus third harmonic 180° out of phase at $t = 0$

Average value of a waveform

The *average*, or *mean*, value of any waveform can be determined in a number of ways but one of the most convenient and simple is the *mid-ordinate rule*. The waveform is divided up into a number of segments along its time axis and then an ordinate is drawn vertically at the middle of each segment upwards from the time axis. The average value of the waveform is then given by:

$$\text{Average value} = \frac{\text{sum of mid-ordinates}}{\text{number of mid-ordinates}} \qquad (5.5)$$

The greater the number of mid-ordinates taken the greater will be the accuracy of the calculated average value but, of course, the work involved will also be greater.

Example 5.5

Calculate the average value of the current waveform shown in Fig. 5.13.

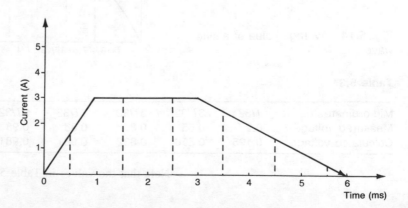

Fig. 5.13

Table 5.2

Mid-ordinate (ms)	0.5	1.5	2.5	3.5	4.5	5.5
Current (A)	1.5	3	3	2.5	1.5	0.5

Solution
Mid-ordinates have been drawn at odd half-millisecond intervals along the
time axis and their values measured. The results obtained are listed in Table
5.2.
From equation (5.5), average current = 12/6 = 2 A.   (*Ans.*)

The sinusoidal waveform

The average value of any alternating waveform that is symmetrical
about the time axis will be zero if taken over one complete cycle
because it has equal positive and negative half-cycles. In all such cases
the average value is taken over one half-cycle. Probably the most
important example of this is the sinusoidal waveform. Figure 5.14
shows the positive half-cycle of a sinusoidal voltage waveform whose
time axis has been divided into eight $T/16$ time intervals, where T
is the periodic time of the waveform.

Mid-ordinates have been drawn in the middle of each time interval
and these have the measured values listed in Table 5.3. Also listed
are the corresponding values calculated using a calculator, e.g., sin
$(T/32)$ = sin 11.25° = 0.195.

From the measured values the average value is 5.06/8 = 0.633 V_m.

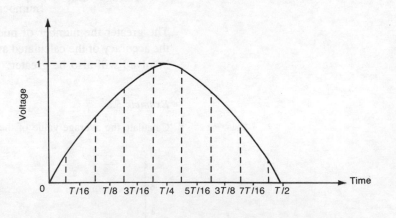

Fig. 5.14 Average value of a sine
wave

Table 5.3

Mid-ordinate	$T/32$	$3T/32$	$5T/32$	$7T/32$	$9T/32$	$11T/32$	$13T/32$	$15T/32$
Measured voltage	0.2	0.55	0.8	0.98	0.98	0.8	0.55	0.2
Calculated voltage	0.195	0.556	0.832	0.981	0.981	0.832	0.556	0.195

Note that the values in Table 5.3 repeat after a quarter of a cycle.

Table 5.4

Mid-ordinate	4.5°	13.5°	22.5°	31.5°	40.5°	49.5°	58.5°	67.5°	76.5°	85.5°
Calculated voltage	0.078	0.233	0.383	0.522	0.649	0.76	0.853	0.924	0.972	0.997

From the calculated values the average value is 5.128/8 = 0.641 V_m.

The average value of a sine wave can be obtained with greater accuracy if a larger number of mid-ordinates are employed. If the time axis of the half-cycle is divided into 20 time intervals, i.e., each of 180°/20 = 9°, the mid-ordinates will then occur at 4.5° and at odd integer multiples of 4.5° as shown in Table 5.4.

Each of these calculated voltages has a corresponding value in the range 90° to 180°. The sum of the calculated values is 6.371 and therefore the average value $= 2 \times 6.371/20 = 0.637 \, V_m$.

This figure is the accurate value for the average value of a sinusoidal voltage or current waveform.

Average value of a sinusoidal voltage wave = 0.637 V_m.   (5.6)
Average value of a sinusoidal current waveform = 0.637 I_m. (5.7)

Example 5.6

Calculate the average value of the current wave $i = 3.5 \sin (\omega t + \pi/4)$ A.

Solution
The peak value of the current is 3.5 A and so the average value is 0.637 × 3.5 = 2.23 A.   (*Ans.*)

The triangular waveform

Figure 5.15 shows a triangular waveform having a peak value of V_m volts. It is clear by inspection that the average value of a half-cycle

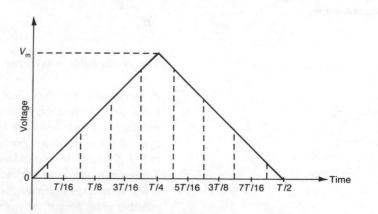

Fig. 5.15 Average value of a triangular wave

Table 5.5

Mid-ordinate	$T/32$	$3T/32$	$5T/32$	$7T/32$	$9T/32$	$11T/32$	$13T/32$	$15T/32$
Voltage	1/8	3/8	5/8	7/8	7/8	5/8	3/8	1/8

The average voltage = $(32/8)/8$ = $0.5V_m$ as expected.

of the waveform is equal to $V_m/2$ and of a complete cycle is zero, but the average value will be calculated to illustrate the method employed.

The time axis of the positive half-cycle has been divided into eight equal intervals of $T/16$. Mid-ordinates have been drawn at $T/32$ and odd multiples of $T/32$ and these mid-ordinates have the values given in Table 5.5.

The square waveform

The square waveform, shown in Fig. 5.16, clearly has an average value over a half-cycle that is equal to its peak value.

$$\text{Average value} = V_m. \tag{5.8}$$

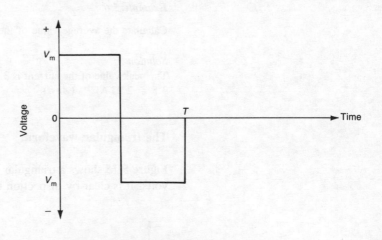

Fig. 5.16 Average value of a square wave

The rectangular waveform

A rectangular waveform will not have equal positive and negative areas, instead either the positive or the negative area will be the larger and the waveform will have an average value taken over a complete cycle that may be either positive or negative. An example is shown in Fig. 5.17 and this wave clearly has an average value that is positive. The average value can be determined using the mid-ordinate rule but it will be quicker to realize that the negative area cancels out an equal positive area. Hence the average voltage is $V_m/3$.

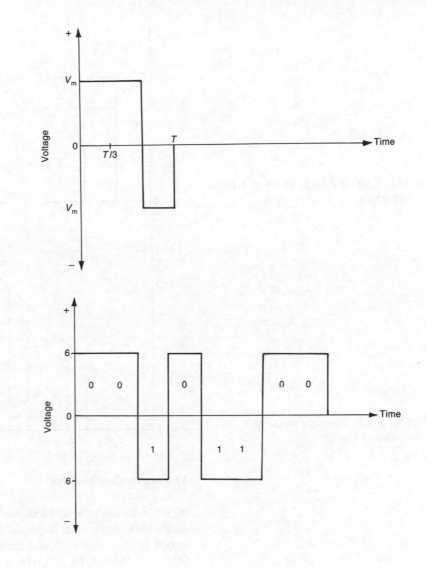

Fig. 5.17 Average value of a rectangular wave

Fig. 5.18

Example 5.7

Calculate the average value of the digital waveform shown in Fig. 5.18.

Solution
The three negative '1' pulses cancel out three of the positive '0' pulses so that the average voltage is $2 \times 6/8 = +1.5 \, \text{V}$.   (*Ans.*)

The pulse waveform

Figure 5.19 shows a pulse waveform in which pulses of duration τ have a periodic time of T. The pulse repetition frequency (p.r.f.) is the number of pulses that occur per second and it is equal to $1/T$. The average value of the waveform is $V_m \tau / T$ volts.

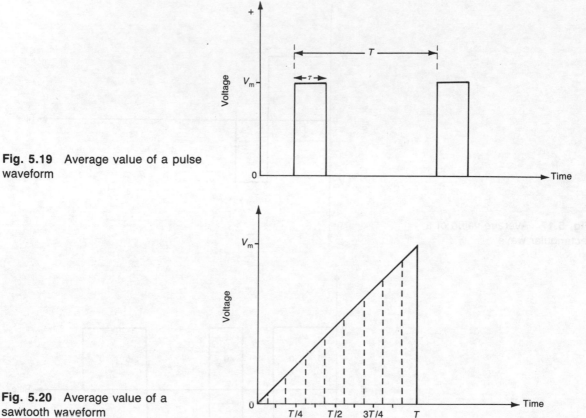

Fig. 5.19 Average value of a pulse waveform

Fig. 5.20 Average value of a sawtooth waveform

The sawtooth waveform

Figure 5.20 shows a sawtooth waveform whose time axis has been divided into eight equal intervals. Mid-ordinates have been erected at odd multiples of $T/16$ and have the values $V_m(1/16 + 3/16 + 5/16 + 7/16 + 9/16 + 11/16 + 13/16 + 15/16)$ and hence the average voltage is $4V_m/8 = V_m/2$. This result could, have course, have been obtained by inspection.

Root mean square value of a waveform

The average value of a waveform is, in many cases, of little importance because it is usually the power that is dissipated by a current that matters and this depends upon the *root mean square* or r.m.s. value of the waveform. The r.m.s., or effective, value of a waveform is the d.c. current, or voltage, that would dissipate the same power in a resistance. The r.m.s. value is equal to the square root of the mean value of the squared waveform. Since the waveform is squared alternate positive and negative half-cycles of the waveform will both give positive values and they are therefore additive. The r.m.s. value of all waveforms is therefore calculated over one complete cycle.

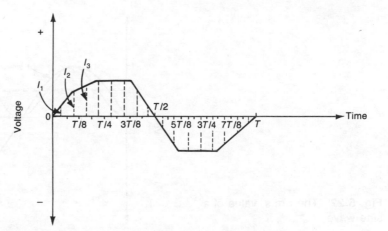

Fig. 5.21 Calculation of r.m.s. value

The a.c. current waveform shown in Fig. 5.21 has had its time axis divided into 16 equal intervals. If the mid-ordinate values of the intervals are I_1, I_2, I_3, etc., the average power dissipated in the first time interval is $I_1^2 R$ watts, in the second time interval is $I_2^2 R$ watts, in the third time interval is $I_3^2 R$ watts, etc. If the d.c. current that would dissipate the same power in the same resistance R is I amps then

$$I^2 R = R(I_1^2 + I_2^2 + I_3^2 + \ldots\ldots I_{16}^2)/16$$
$$\text{or}\quad I = \sqrt{(I_1^2 + I_2^2 + I_3^2 + \ldots\ldots I_{16}^2)/16} \tag{5.9}$$

The sinusoidal waveform

When a sine wave is squared the resultant waveform is always positive and so the mean value of the squared waveform can be determined over a complete cycle. The values listed in Table 5.4 for a sinusoidal waveform are repeated in Table 5.6 with the addition of the squared values. The sum of the calculated values is 5. Hence

$$(\text{Average voltage})^2 = 2 \times 5/20 = 0.5\, V_m^2.$$
$$\text{The r.m.s. voltage} = \sqrt{0.5} = 0.707\, V_m = V_m/\sqrt{2}. \tag{5.10}$$

This result can be obtained in a different way. When a sinusoidal voltage wave of peak value 1 V is squared the resultant waveform is at twice the frequency and has a mean value of 1/2 V. This is shown by Fig. 5.22. The $\sin^2 \omega t$ waveform can be considered to consist of the summation of a d.c. voltage of 1/2 V and a negative cosine wave of peak value 1/2 V and of frequency $2\omega t$. Over a complete cycle the

Table 5.6

Mid-ordinate	4.5°	13.5°	22.5°	31.5°	40.5°	49.5°	58.5°	67.5°	76.5°	85.5°
Calculated value	0.078	0.233	0.383	0.522	0.649	0.76	0.853	0.924	0.972	0.997
(Calculated value)^2	–	0.054	0.147	0.273	0.421	0.578	0.728	0.854	0.945	0.994

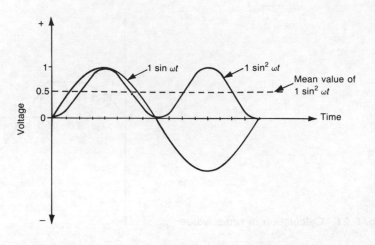

Fig. 5.22 The r.m.s. value of a sine wave

mean value of the cosine wave is zero and hence the average value of $1 \sin^2 \omega t$ over one cycle is $V_{av} = V_m/2$. The r.m.s. voltage is equal to the square root of this, i.e., $V = V_m/\sqrt{2}$ as before.

It is the usual practice to express the magnitude of a sinusoidal waveform in terms of its r.m.s. value and unless stated otherwise any voltage should be assumed to be the r.m.s. value. The r.m.s. voltage, or current, is represented by a capital letter without a suffix.

Example 5.8

For the sinusoidal voltage wave $v = 325 \sin(100\pi t + 30°)$ volts determine (*a*) its peak value, (*b*) its average value, (*c*) its r.m.s. value, (*d*) its frequency, and (*e*) its instantaneous value when $t = 1$ ms.

Solution

(*a*) $V_m = 325$ V.   (*Ans.*)
(*b*) $V_{av} = 0.637 \times 325 = 207$ V.   (*Ans.*)
(*c*) $V = 0.707 \times 325 = 230$ V.   (*Ans.*)
(*d*) $f = 100\pi/2\pi = 50$ Hz.   (*Ans.*)
(*e*) $v = 325 \sin(100\pi \times 1 \times 10^{-3} + 30°) = 325 \sin 48°$
       $= 241.5$ V.   (*Ans.*)

The triangular waveform

The r.m.s. value of the triangular waveform given in Fig. 5.15 can be obtained from the values given in Table 5.5. Squaring the values used to get the average value of the waveform gives

$$V^2 = 2 \times V_m^2[(1 + 9 + 25 + 49 + 49 + 25 + 9 + 1)/64]/16$$
$$= 2V_m^2[168/(64 \times 16)] = 0.328V_m^2.$$

The r.m.s. value $V = \sqrt{(0.328V_m^2)} = 0.573V_m = V_m/\sqrt{3}$

(5.11)

Example 5.9

A triangular wave has a peak voltage of 6 V. Calculate (*a*) its average value over half a cycle, and (*b*) its r.m.s. value.

Solution

(*a*) $V_{av} = 6/2 = 3$ V.   (*Ans.*)

(*b*) $V = 6/\sqrt{3} = 3.46$ V.   (*Ans.*)

The square waveform

When the square waveform of Fig. 5.16 is squared the resultant wave has a constant value of V_m^2 and hence both its peak and average values are equal to V_m^2. The r.m.s. voltage is the square root of this value, therefore

$$V = V_m = V_{av} \tag{5.12}$$

The r.m.s. value of a rectangular waveform is equal to the mean value and so it will depend upon the relative time durations of its positive and negative voltages.

The sawtooth waveform

To obtain the r.m.s. value of a sawtooth wave it is necessary to square the values given on p. 82. Hence,

$$V_{av}^2 = V_m^2[(1 + 9 + 25 + 49 + 81 + 121 + 169 + 225)/256]/8$$
$$= V_m^2[680/(256 \times 8)] = 0.332V_m^2$$

The r.m.s. value $V = \sqrt{(0.332)^2} = 0.576V_m = V_m/\sqrt{3}$.   (*Ans.*)

Example 5.10

Calculate the average and mean values of the waveform given in Fig. 5.23.

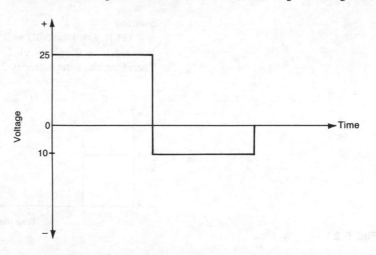

Fig. 5.23

Solution

$$V_{av} = (25 - 10)/2 = 7.5\,V. \quad (Ans.)$$
$$V = \sqrt{[(25^2 + 10^2)/2]} = 19\,V. \quad (Ans.)$$

Form factor

The form factor of an a.c. waveform is equal to the ratio given in equation (5.13), i.e.,

$$\text{Form factor} = (\text{r.m.s. value})/(\text{average value}) \quad (5.13)$$

The form factor of a waveform is an indication of how far from being of square shape the waveform is. The higher the form factor the more 'peaky' is the waveform. Values for some of the waveforms already discussed are given in Table 5.7.

The peak, or crest, factor of a waveform is given by equation (5.14).

Table 5.7

Waveform	Peak value	Average value	r.m.s. value	Form factor	Peak factor
Sinusoidal	V_m	$0.637V_m$	$0.707V_m$	1.11	1.414
Triangular	V_m	$V_m/2$	$V_m/\sqrt{3}$	1.155	1.73
Square	V_m	V_m	V_m	1	1
Pulse	V_m	$V_m\varsigma/T$	$V_m\varsigma/T$	1	t/ς
Sawtooth	V_m	$V_m/2$	$V_m/\sqrt{3}$	1.155	1.73

$$\text{Peak factor} = (\text{peak value})/(\text{r.m.s. value}) \quad (5.14)$$

Two different waveforms might have the same form factors *or* the same peak factors but *not* both.

Example 5.11

Calculate the form factor of the waveforms shown in Figs. 5.24(*a*) and (*b*).

Solution

(*a*) $V_{av} = 1 \times 5/10 = 0.5\,V.$
$V = \sqrt{[(1^2 + 0^2)/2]} = \sqrt{0.5} = 0.707\,V.$
Therefore, the form factor is $2/\sqrt{2} = \sqrt{2}.$ (*Ans.*)

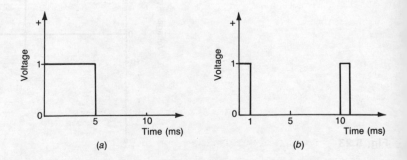

Fig. 5.24

(*a*)   (*b*)

(b) $V_{av} = 1 \times 1/10 = 0.1$ V.
$V = \sqrt{0.1} = 0.3162$ V.
Therefore the form factor is $0.3162/0.1 = 3.162$. *(Ans.)*

The phasor representation of sinusoidal waveforms

A *phasor* has a length that is directly proportional to the magnitude, peak or r.m.s., of the current or the voltage that it represents. A phasor is drawn at a specified angle to a reference line that is usually in the horizontal direction. In the derivation of the sinusoidal waveform on p. 70 a phasor was made to rotate about its origin with a constant angular velocity of ω radians per second. When phasors are used to represent currents and/or voltages at the same frequency they all rotate with the same angular velocity and so they have zero motion relative to one another. This means that the phasors may be assumed to be stationary and they are so drawn in a *phasor diagram*.

Addition of two phasors

Figure 5.25 shows two phasors V_1 and V_2 that have a phase angle of ϕ_1 between them. The phasor V_1 lies in the horizontal direction and so it is (usually) taken as the reference phasor. Addition of the two phasors can be carried out by completing the parallelogram, as shown by the dotted lines, and then drawing the diagonal $0V$ to obtain the resultant phasor V. Although simple in principle the method requires careful drawing of both the lengths of the phasors and of the angle between them; it is therefore a rather lengthy and not very convenient procedure. Sometimes neither of the two phasors are in the reference horizontal direction as shown by Fig. 5.25(b) but the procedure is the same; one of the phasors must be taken as the reference and the resultant found and this can be expressed relative to the horizontal if required. For example, in Fig. 5.25(b) phasor V_1

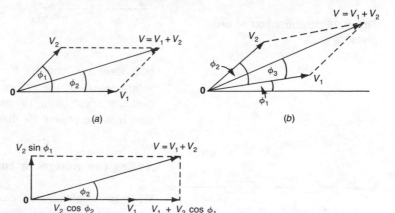

Fig. 5.25 Addition of two phasors

is at angle ϕ_1 to the horizontal and phasor V_2 is at angle $\phi_2 + \phi_1$ to the horizontal; the resultant phasor V is at angle ϕ_3 to V_1 and hence at angle $\phi_1 + \phi_3$ to the horizontal.

The alternative method of determining the resultant phasor is to resolve each phasor into its horizontal and vertical components and then use Pythagoras's theorem to find the resultant. This method is illustrated by Fig. 5.25(c) which refers to (a). Phasor V_1 lies in the horizontal direction and so it has zero vertical component; phasor V_2 is at an angle ϕ_1 to the horizontal and so it has both a horizontal component and a vertical component. The horizontal component of V_2 is $V_2 \cos \phi_1$ and the vertical component is $V_2 \sin \phi_1$. The total horizontal component is hence $V_1 + V_2 \cos \phi_1$ and, using Pythagoras, the resultant phasor V has a magnitude of

$$\sqrt{[(V_1 + V_2 \cos \phi_1)^2 + (V_2^2 \sin^2\phi_1)]}$$

and makes angle

$$\phi_2 = \tan^{-1}[V_2 \sin \phi_1/(V_1 + V_2 \cos \phi_1)]$$

to the horizontal.

Subtraction of two phasors

When the difference between two phasors is to be calculated the phasor that is to be subtracted from the other phasor should have its direction reversed on the phasor diagram. The reversed phasor can then be added to the other phasor to obtain the magnitude and angle of their difference. Two cases are illustrated by Figs 5.26(a) and (b) which

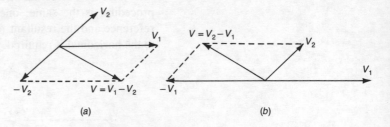

(a) (b)

Fig. 5.26 Subtraction of two phasors

both show two phasors V_1 and V_2. In (a) the phasor V_2 is to be subtracted from the phasor V_1 and so it is V_2 that has had its direction reversed; in (b) the difference $V_2 - V_1$ is wanted and so now it is the phasor V_1 that is reversed in direction.

Adding two voltages or currents

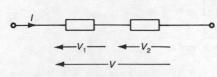

Fig. 5.27 Voltages in series

When two components are connected in series, as in Fig. 5.27, and a current I is allowed to flow, voltages V_1 and V_2 will be developed across the components. If the two components are both purely resistive the two voltage drops will be in phase with both the current and each

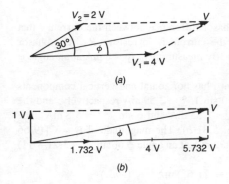

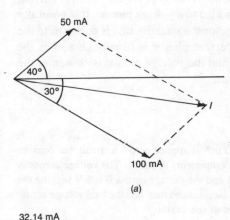

Fig. 5.28

other. The total voltage V is then merely the arithmetic sum of the individual voltage drops V_1 and V_2. If, however, either or both of the components is *not* purely resistive the two voltages will not be in phase with one another and their resultant voltage V must be determined with the aid of a phasor diagram. If, for example, $v_1 = 4 \sin \omega t$ and $v_2 = 2 \sin (\omega t + 30°)$ then the phasor diagram is shown by Fig. 5.28(a). The lengths of the two phasors have been drawn proportional to the peak values of the two voltages but phasors are often drawn using r.m.s. values. By measurement from the figure the peak value of the resultant voltage V is 5.8 V and the angle ϕ is 10°. Alternatively, the phasor that represents voltage v_2 can be resolved into its horizontal and vertical components; the horizontal component is $2 \cos 30° = 1.732$ V and the vertical component is $2 \sin 30° = 1$ V. The phasor diagram for this is shown in Fig. 5.28(b); the resultant voltage can be determined by measurement but, more accurately, $V = \sqrt{(5.732^2 + 1^2)} = 5.819$ V. The angle $\phi = \tan^{-1}(1/5.732) = 9.9°$.

Example 5.12

Two currents $i_1 = 70.7 \sin (\omega t + 40°)$ mA and $i_2 = 141.4 \sin (\omega t - 30°)$ mA flow in a resistance of 1 kΩ. Draw the phasor diagram of the currents and hence determine (a) the r.m.s. value of the total current, (b) the phase angle of the total current relative to (i) i_1 and (ii) the horizontal, and (c) the mean power dissipated in the resistance.

Solution

The phasor diagram of the currents is shown in Fig. 5.29(a); r.m.s. values are used. By measurement from the diagram the resultant current is 126 mA at an angle of 48° to i_1 and 8° to the horizontal.   (*Ans.*)

The mean power dissipated in the 1 kΩ resistance is $(126 \times 10^{-3})^2 \times 1000 = 15.88$ W.   (*Ans.*)

Alternatively, resolving i_1 into its horizontal and vertical components gives $50 \cos 40° = 38.3$ mA and $50 \sin 40° = 32.14$ mA respectively. Similarly, the horizontal and vertical components of i_2 are $100 \cos (-30°) = 86.6$ mA and $100 \sin (-30°) = -50$ mA respectively. These components have been drawn in Fig. 5.29(b). The r.m.s. resultant current has a magnitude of $\sqrt{[(38.3 + 86.6)^2 + (50 - 32.14)^2]} = 126.17$ mA at an angle of $\tan^{-1}(-17.86/124.9) = 8.1°$.   (*Ans.*)

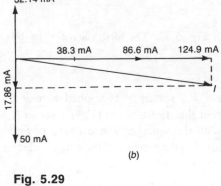

Fig. 5.29

Example 5.13

Determine the expression for the current i_1 flowing in resistor R_1 in the circuit shown by Fig. 5.30.

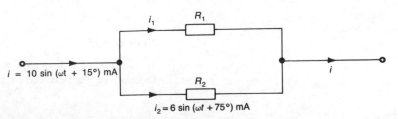

$i = 10 \sin (\omega t + 15°)$ mA

$i_2 = 6 \sin (\omega t + 75°)$ mA

Fig. 5.30

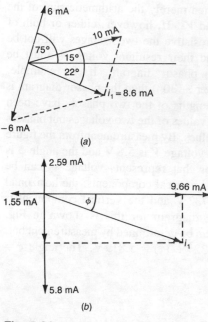

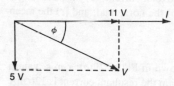

Fig. 5.31

Solution

The current i_1 is equal to the phasor difference between the current i that is flowing into the circuit and the current i_2 in resistor R_2. The phasor diagram is given in Fig. 5.31(*a*). By measurement $i_1 = 8$ mA at an angle ϕ of $-22°$ to the horizontal.

Alternatively, the input current i has horizontal and vertical components of $10 \cos 15° = 9.66$ mA and $10 \sin 15° = 2.59$ mA respectively, and the components of i_2 are $6 \cos 75° = 1.55$ mA and $6 \sin 75° = 5.8$ mA. The phasor diagram is shown in Fig. 5.31(*b*). The magnitude of $i_1 = \sqrt{[(9.66 - 1.55)^2 + (5.8 - 2.59)^2]} = 8.72$ mA at an angle ϕ of $\tan^{-1}(-3.21/8.11) = -21.6°$.

Therefore, $i_1 = 8.72 \sin(\omega t - 21.6°)$ mA. (*Ans.*)

Both currents and voltages may be drawn on the same phasor diagram to illustrate the phase difference(s) between them. A current phasor cannot, of course, be added to a voltage phasor. It is generally best to make the reference phasor the quantity that is common to the circuit; this means that the current phasor is usually chosen as the reference for a series circuit and the voltage phasor is chosen as the reference for a parallel circuit.

Example 5.14

The current $i = 5 \sin 60\pi \times 10^3 t$ mA is applied across a circuit that consists of the series connection of two components A and B. The voltage across A is 11 V in phase with the current and the voltage across B is 5 V lagging the current by 90°. Draw the phasor diagram and then find the total voltage across the circuit and its phase relative to the current.

Solution

The phasor diagram is given in Fig. 5.32. The total voltage V is, by measurement, 12 V at angle $\phi = -24°$. (*Ans.*)

Fig. 5.32

Power in an a.c. circuit

When a sinusoidal voltage $v = V_m \sin \omega t$ V is applied across a resistance of R ohms the current that flows is $i = (V_m/R) \sin \omega t$ A and the current is in phase with the voltage. The *average* power dissipated in the resistance is equal to the product of the r.m.s. values of the current and the voltage, i.e.,

$$P = (I_m/\sqrt{2})(V_m/\sqrt{2}) = I_m V_m/2 = IV \text{ watts.} \qquad (5.15)$$

Since $I = V/R$ the power dissipated can also be written in the form

$$P = I^2 R = V^2/R \text{ watts.} \qquad (5.16)$$

Example 5.15

The voltage $v = 2.5 \sin(20\pi \times 10^3 t)$ volts is applied to a 1000 Ω resistor. Calculate (*a*) the peak current and (*b*) the power dissipated.

Solution
    (a) $I_m = 2.5/1000 = 2.5$ mA.   (*Ans.*)
    (b) $P = (2.5 \times 10^{-3})/\sqrt{2} \times 2.5/\sqrt{2} = 3.125$ mW.   (*Ans.*)

Example 5.16

A resistor dissipates 600 W when it is connected across a 240 V a.c. supply. What voltage will be required for the same resistor to dissipate 400 W? An oven needs an average power of 600 W when it is heated by two resistors that are each connected across a 240 V a.c. supply. One of the resistors is permanently connected to the supply and it dissipates 500 W continuously. The other resistor is switched on and off cyclically with equal on and off times. Calculate the values of the two resistors.

Solution
    $600 = 240^2/R$, $R = 96\,\Omega$. $V = \sqrt{(96 \times 400)} = 196$ V.
    $R_1 = 240^2/500 = 115.2\,\Omega$.   (*Ans.*)
R_2 must dissipate 100 W on average and, since it is switched on and off at equal intervals of time when it is carrying current, it must dissipate 200 W. Hence,
    $R_2 = 240^2/200 = 288\,\Omega$.   (*Ans.*)

Rectification

All electronic equipment requires a power supply to provide the necessary d.c. operating voltages and currents. Essentially a power supply consists of a mains transformer to convert the 240 V supply voltage to the lower value required by the equipment, a rectifier which converts an a.c. voltage into a d.c. voltage, a reservoir capacitor, and a filter circuit. Rectification is the conversion of an a.c. voltage into a d.c. voltage by the application of simple switching. There are three basic types of rectifier circuits in common use; namely the half-wave rectifier, the full-wave rectifier, and the bridge rectifier.

The basic half-wave rectifier is shown in Fig. 5.33(*a*) and it consists merely of a diode connected in series with the secondary winding of the mains transformer and the load R_L. The diode will only conduct current during the half-cycles of the transformed voltage V_S that make the point A positive relative to the point B. The current therefore flows as a series of half sine-wave pulses. Since the load is resistive the voltage V_L developed across the load has the same waveform as the load current as shown by Fig. 5.33(*b*). Clearly the load voltage, although unidirectional, varies considerably and it is not suitable for other than simple applications such as battery charging.

If a *reservoir capacitor* C_1 is connected in parallel with the load as shown by Fig. 5.34(*a*) the load voltage can be stopped from falling to zero after every positive half-cycle of the transformer secondary voltage V_S. Each time the diode conducts the current it passes charges up the capacitor. The diode continues to conduct as long as V_S is more positive than the capacitor voltage; whenever the

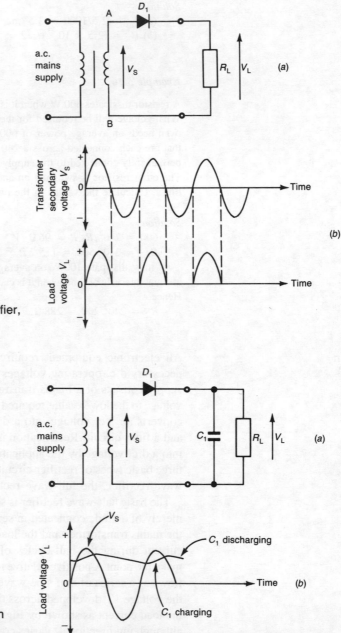

Fig. 5.33 (a) The half-wave rectifier, (b) waveforms

Fig. 5.34 Half-wave rectifier with reservoir capacitor

capacitor voltage is more positive than V_S the diode becomes non-conducting and the capacitor will then discharge through the load resistance. When the voltage V_S becomes more positive than the capacitor voltage the diode conducts again and the capacitor voltage rises. The component values are chosen to ensure that the capacitor does not discharge very much between its charging current pulses and then the average load voltage is only slightly less than the peak

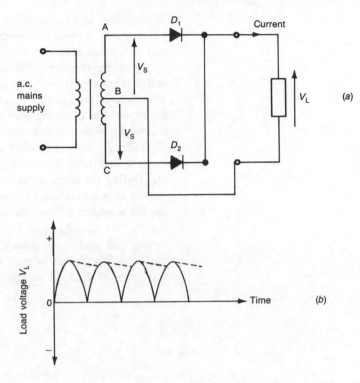

Fig. 5.35 (a) The full-wave rectifier,
(b) waveforms

value of V_S. The waveforms of both V_S and the load voltage V_L are
shown by Fig. 5.34(b).

The load voltage is not quite constant but, instead, exhibits some
fluctuations about the mean voltage. It may be considered to consist
of the sum of a d.c. voltage, equal to the mean voltage, and an a.c.
ripple voltage. The ripple voltage is at the frequency of the mains
supply voltage, i.e., 50 Hz. This ripple voltage is undesirable and
it is usually removed by a *filter circuit*.

In practice, the half-wave rectifier circuit is little used since better
results can be obtained from the full-wave rectifier circuit shown in
Fig. 5.35(a). The secondary winding of the transformer is centre-
tapped so that equal voltages V_S are applied to the the two diodes
D_1 and D_2. During the half-cycles of the mains supply voltage that
take point A positive with respect to point B, and point C negative
with respect to point B, diode D_1 conducts but diode D_2 does not.
Current therefore flows in the load in the direction indicated by the
arrow. When the following half-cycle of the mains supply input takes
the point A negative, and the point C positive, with respect to point
B diode D_2 conducts and diode D_1 does not conduct. The load
current flows in the load in the same direction as before. The
waveform of the current flowing in the load, and hence of the load
voltage, is shown by Fig. 5.35(b). As with the half-wave circuit a
reservoir capacitor can be connected across the load to give a more
nearly constant load voltage; the effect of the reservoir capacitor would

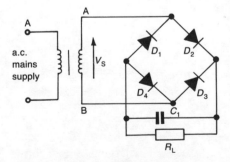

Fig. 5.36 The bridge rectifier

be that shown by the dotted line. Once again a ripple voltage is present but now it is at twice the mains frequency, i.e., at 100 Hz, and this makes it much easier to filter out.

The *bridge rectifier* provides an alternative method of full-wave rectification and its circuit is given in Fig. 5.36. The circuit has the advantage of not needing a centre-tapped transformer but this is at the expense of requiring four diodes. During the half-cycles of the mains supply voltage that make the point A positive relative to point B, diodes D_2 and D_4 conduct while D_1 and D_3 are non-conducting. Current then flows from point A to point B via D_2, the load R_L, and D_4. During the alternate half-cycles when point A is negative with respect to point B diodes D_1 and D_3 are conducting and D_2 and D_4 are not conducting. Now the current flows from point B to point A via D_3, the load R_L, and D_1. The current therefore always flows through the load in the same direction. The reservoir capacitor has the same function as in the other full-wave circuit and hence the waveform of the load voltage is that shown by Fig. 5.35(b).

6 Single-phase a.c. circuits

The vast majority of the circuits in which an a.c. current flows consist of the series, or the parallel, or the series–parallel, connection of two, or all three, of the components resistance, inductance and capacitance. Although the voltage developed across a resistance is in phase with the current flowing in the resistance this is not true for either an inductor or a capacitor. In the case of an inductor the voltage leads the current by 90° and in the case of a capacitor the current leads the voltage by 90°. It is therefore necessary to use phasor diagrams to represent the currents and voltages in an a.c. circuit.

Pure inductance

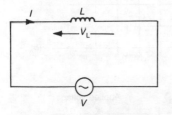

Fig. 6.1 Pure inductance

Figure 6.1 shows an a.c. circuit that consists merely of a source of a.c. voltage V volts connected across an inductor of L henrys that is assumed to have zero resistance, i.e., no copper or iron losses. From equation (4.12) the back e.m.f. e induced into the windings of the inductor is equal to $-L\mathrm{d}i/\mathrm{d}t$, where, as before, $\mathrm{d}i/\mathrm{d}t$ means the 'rate of change of current in amperes/second'. Since the induced voltage depends upon the rate of change of the current and not the other way around it is usual to assume that the current is of sinusoidal waveshape as shown by Fig. 6.2(a).

At time $t = 0$ the current is zero and increasing towards its positive peak value with its maximum positive rate of change; as the peak value is neared the positive rate of change of current decreases and it falls to zero when the positive peak occurs at time $t = T/4$, where T is the periodic time of the waveform. The current then starts to fall towards its maximum negative value, slowly at first and then with an ever increasing negative rate of change, until the maximum rate of change of current is reached when the current passes through 0A and becomes negative (i.e., the current flows in the opposite direction). As the current increases negatively its negative rate of change falls and becomes instantaneously zero when the current has reached its negative peak value at time $t = 3T/4$. The current then falls towards 0A with a positive rate of change and when it passes through 0A to become positive another cycle is repeated. The waveform of the rate of change of the current is shown by Fig. 6.2(b) and it can be seen to be of cosinusoidal waveshape.

The e.m.f. induced into the inductor by the changing current is $-L\mathrm{d}i/\mathrm{d}t$ and so it is at all times in anti-phase with the $\mathrm{d}i/\mathrm{d}t$ waveform. The waveform of the induced voltage is shown by Fig. 6.2(c). The applied voltage V must overcome the 'back e.m.f.' in order for the

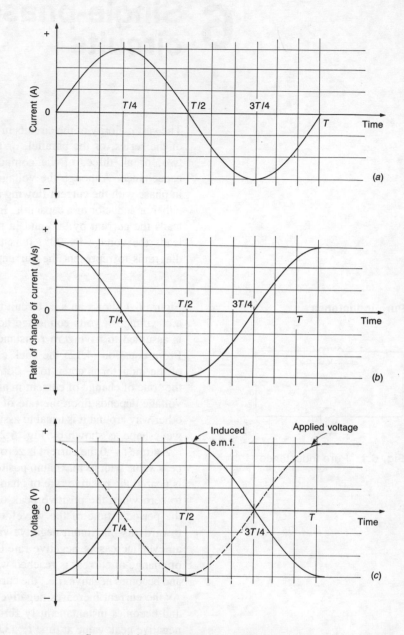

Fig. 6.2 Current and voltage waveforms for a pure inductance

current to flow and this means that it must be 180° out-of-phase with the induced voltage. The waveform of the applied voltage is shown by the dotted line in Fig. 6.2(c); clearly, it leads the current waveform by 90°.

If the expression for the current is $i = I_m \sin \omega t$ then the applied voltage is given by $v = V_m \sin (\omega t + 90°)$. Alternatively, the applied voltage can be written as $v = V_m \sin \omega t$ and the current as $i = I_m \sin (\omega t - 90°)$.

The phasor diagram showing the phase relationship between the current and voltage in a purely inductive circuit is shown in Fig. 6.3.

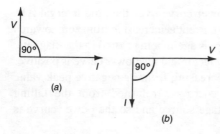

Fig. 6.3 Phasor diagrams for a pure inductance

Either Fig. 6.3(a) or (b) may be used depending upon which phasor is regarded as the reference.

Example 6.1

The current $i = 50 \sin 2000t$ mA is applied to an inductor of 250 mH. What is the expression for the instantaneous voltage across the inductor?

Solution

The reactance of the inductor is $2000 \times 0.25 = 500\ \Omega$ and so the required expression is $v = 157.1 \sin (2000t + 90°)$ V.   (*Ans.*)

Power

Figure 6.4 shows the waveforms of the voltage applied to, and the current flowing in, a pure inductor. They are taken from Figs 6.2(a) and (c). The instantaneous power dissipated in the circuit is obtained by multiplying together the instantaneous values of current and voltage at each instant in time. Whenever either the current or the voltage is instantaneously zero the instantaneous power will also be zero. When the current is increasing from zero towards its positive peak value the magnetic flux set up around the inductor is also increasing in the direction indicated earlier (p. 32). This flux is a form of stored energy and so the positive area 0A represents the energy supplied by the a.c. voltage source in setting up the magnetic field (equal to $LI_m^2/2$ J). When the current is decreasing from its positive peak value towards zero the magnetic flux linking the inductance is also falling; the direction of the induced e.m.f. is now reversed and, from Lenz's law, tends to oppose the fall in the current. Both the induced e.m.f. and the current now act in the same direction and so energy is returned to the a.c. voltage source. This is represented in the figure

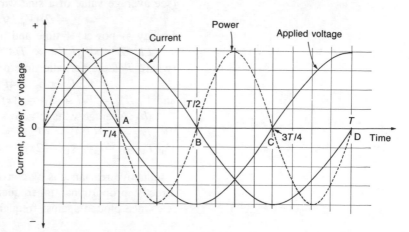

Fig. 6.4 Power in a pure inductor

by the negative area of the power curve over the time interval AB. In the next time interval BC the current is increasing from zero towards the negative peak value, energy is again being stored in the magnetic field that is set up around the inductor and the power curve is positive. Lastly, when the current is decreasing from its negative peak value towards zero, interval CD, energy is returned from the falling magnetic field to the a.c. voltage source and so the power curve is once again negative.

The power curve is shown in Fig. 6.4 by the dotted line; it can be seen to be of sinusoidal waveshape at twice the frequency of the current and the voltage waves. The power curve is symmetrical about the 0 V axis and in one complete cycle of the current (or voltage) waveform has equal positive and negative areas. This means that the *average power* over one complete cycle is zero.

Inductive reactance

Inductive reactance X_L is the ability of an inductance to oppose the flow of an a.c. current through that inductance. It is equal to the ratio of the voltage V across the inductance to the current I flowing in the inductance, i.e., $X_L = V/I$ ohms. Inductive reactance is analogous to electrical resistance except that zero power is dissipated. The magnitude of the inductive reactance depends upon both the inductance L in henrys, and the frequency f, in hertz, of the current, i.e.,

$$X_L = 2\pi fL \quad \Omega. \tag{6.1}$$

This important expression can be obtained in the following ways:

(*a*) During a positive area of the power waveform shown in Fig. 6.4 the average power is equal to:

average power = peak power $\times 2/\pi$.

(see average value of a sine wave on p. 79.)

$$= 2[(V_m/\sqrt{2})(I_m/\sqrt{2})]/\pi = V_m I_m/\pi.$$

Energy = power $\times$ time and hence

$LI_m^2/2 = V_m I_m/\pi \times T/4$

(where T is the periodic time of the current waveform)

$$= V_m I_m/\pi \times 1/4f$$

and $V_m/I_m = V/I = X_L = 2\pi fL$ ohms. $\tag{6.2}$

(*b*) Average voltage across inductance = $L \times$ average di/dt

$2V_m/\pi = I_m/(T/4) = 4I_m/T = 4fI_m$

$V_m/I_m = V/I = X_L = 2\pi fL$ ohms. $\tag{6.2 again.}$

Inductive reactance is by convention taken to be positive and it is directly proportional to frequency. Figure 6.5 shows inductive reactance plotted against frequency.

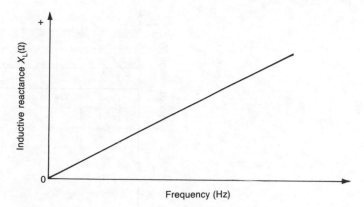

Fig. 6.5 Inductive reactance plotted against frequency

Example 6.2

Calculate the reactance of a 1 mH inductor at a frequency of (*a*) 3 kHz, and (*b*) 3 MHz. (*c*) Calculate the current that flows when 2 V at 3 MHz is applied across the inductor.

Solution

(*a*) $X_L = 2\pi \times 3 \times 10^3 \times 1 \times 10^{-3} = 18.85\,\Omega.$ (*Ans.*)
(*b*) $X_L = 2\pi \times 3 \times 10^6 \times 1 \times 10^{-3} = 18.85\,k\Omega.$ (*Ans.*)
(*c*) $I = V/X_L = 2/(18.85 \times 10^3) = 106\,\mu A.$ (*Ans.*)

Example 6.3

The voltage $v = 25 \sin(4000\pi t)$ volts is applied across a pure inductance of 25 mH. (*a*) Obtain an expression for the current. (*b*) Determine the r.m.s. current. (*c*) Calculate the power dissipated in the inductance.

Solution

(*a*) $X_L = 4000\pi \times 25 \times 10^{-3} = 314.2\,\Omega.$ The peak current is $25/314.2 = 79.57\,mA$ and hence $i = 79.57 \sin(4000\pi t - 90°)\,mA.$
   (*Ans.*)

(*b*) $I = 79.57/\sqrt{2} = 56.27\,mA.$ (*Ans.*)
(*c*) The power dissipated in a pure inductance is zero.   (*Ans.*)

Pure capacitance

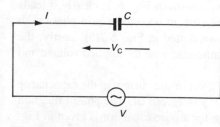

Fig. 6.6 Pure capacitance

Figure 6.6 shows a simple circuit consisting of a capacitance C connected across a source of a.c. voltage V volts. The relationship between the charge Q, in coulombs, on the plates of the capacitance and the voltage V, in volts, across the capacitance is $Q = VC$. If this charge is stored in a time of t seconds the average rate of change of the charge is $Q/t = CV/t = C\,dV_C/dt = -C\,dV/dt$ (since the capacitance voltage is always of the opposite polarity to the applied voltage). At any instant the current flowing is $i = -dQ/dt$. The negative sign indicates that the flow of current is from the voltage source to the capacitance and against the polarity of the capacitance

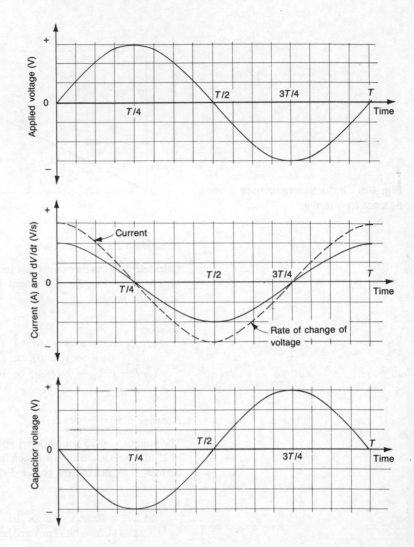

Fig. 6.7 Current and voltage waveforms for a pure capacitance

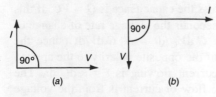

Fig. 6.8 Phasor diagrams for a pure capacitance

voltage V_C. Hence $i = C \, dV/dt$. The waveforms of the applied voltage V, dV/dt and i, and the capacitance voltage V_C are shown in Fig. 6.7. The applied voltage V is shown in Fig. 6.7(a) and it is assumed to be of sinusoidal waveform. The waveform of the rate of change of the applied voltage has been obtained in the same way as the rate of change of current waveform in Fig. 6.2; clearly it leads the applied voltage by 90°. The current waveform is in phase with the dV/dt waveform and is shown dotted in Fig. 6.7(b). Lastly, the capacitor voltage is always in antiphase with the applied voltage and this is shown by Fig. 6.7(c).

If the applied voltage is $v = V_m \sin \omega t$ the current in the capacitance is given by $i = I_m \sin (\omega t + 90°) = I_m \cos \omega t$. The phasor diagram showing the current and voltage for a pure capacitor is given in Fig. 6.8; either Fig. 6.8(a) or (b) could be used depending upon which phasor is chosen to be the reference.

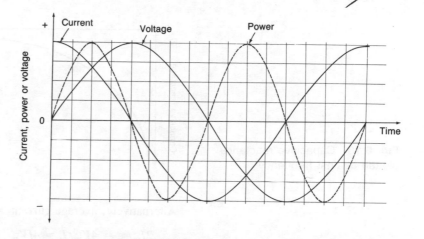

Fig. 6.9 Power in a pure capacitance

Power

The current and voltage waveforms for a capacitance connected to a sinusoidal voltage source are shown in Fig. 6.9. At any instant the instantaneous power dissipated in the capacitance is equal to the product of the instantaneous current and the instantaneous voltage. When either the instantaneous current or the instantaneous voltage is zero the instantaneous power will also be zero. During those intervals of time when both the current and the voltage are positive, and when both the instantaneous current and the instantaneous voltage are negative, the power curve is positive. Whenever either the instantaneous current or the instantaneous voltage is negative and the other is positive the power curve will be negative. The power curve is shown dotted in the figure.

Over one complete cycle of the current, or the voltage, waveform the average power is equal to zero since there are equal areas both above and below the 0 V axis. The areas above the axis represent the energy used in charging the capacitance; the areas below the axis represent the energy that is returned to the a.c. voltage source when the capacitance is discharged. The peak power is $V_m I_m/2$ watts.

Capacitive reactance

The reactance X_C of a capacitance represents the opposition of that capacitance to the flow of an a.c. current and it is equal to the ratio (applied voltage)/current. During the first quarter of the periodic time of the voltage, or current, waveform, energy is taken from the a.c. voltage source to establish the electric field between the plates of the capacitance. The energy used is stored in the capacitor and it is equal to $W = CV_m^2/2$ J. Therefore,

$$CV_m^2/2 = V_m I_m/2 \times 2/\pi \times T/4 = V_m I_m/4\pi f.$$
$$X_C = V_m/I_m = V/I = 1/2\pi fC \quad \text{ohms.} \tag{6.3}$$

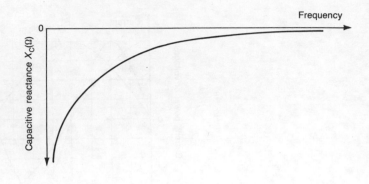

Fig. 6.10 Capacitive reactance plotted against frequency

Alternatively, average current $= C \times$ average dV/dt

$$2I_m/\pi = 4V_m/T = 4fV_m$$
$$X_C = V_m/I_m = V/I = 1/2\pi fC, \text{ as before.}$$

Capacitive reactance is inversely proportional to frequency and so the graph of reactance plotted against frequency has the shape shown in Fig. 6.10. By convention capacitive reactance is negative and its graph is usually drawn below the zero reactance axis as shown. At zero and very low frequencies the reactance of a capacitance is very large but it falls with increase in frequency and reaches a low value at high frequencies.

Example 6.4

Calculate the reactance of a 220 pF capacitor at (*a*) 3 kHz, (*b*) 3 MHz, and (*c*) 30 MHz. (*d*) An a.c. voltage of 2 V at 3 MHz is applied across the capacitor. Calculate the current.

Solution

(*a*) $X_C = 1/(2\pi \times 3000 \times 220 \times 10^{-12}) = 241.14 \text{ k}\Omega.$ (*Ans.*)
(*b*) $X_C = 1/(2\pi \times 3 \times 10^6 \times 220 \times 10^{-12}) = 241 \,\Omega.$ (*Ans.*)
(*c*) $X_C = 241/10 = 24.1 \,\Omega.$ (*Ans.*)
(*d*) $I = V/X_C = 2/241 = 8.3 \text{ mA.}$ (*Ans.*)

Resistance and inductance in series

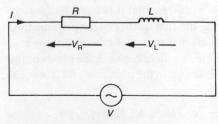

Fig. 6.11 Resistance and inductance in series

Figure 6.11 shows a resistance of R ohms connected in series with an inductance of L henrys with an a.c. voltage source of V volts at frequency f Hz applied to the circuit. A practical inductor possesses inevitable self-resistance due to both conductor and iron losses; this resistance is always considered to be a part of the total resistance of the circuit and included in with R. A current of I amps flows in the circuit and develops a voltage $V_R = IR$ across the resistance, and a voltage $V_L = IX_L$ across the inductance. Voltage V_R is in phase with the current but the voltage V_L leads the current by 90°. This is shown by the phasor diagram given in Fig. 6.12. Since the current is common to both components its phasor is taken as the reference phasor and so it has been drawn in the horizontal direction.

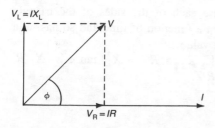

Fig. 6.12 Phasor diagram for *R* and *L* in series

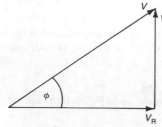

Fig. 6.13 Voltage triangle for *R* and *L* in series

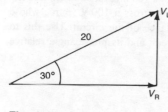

Fig. 6.14

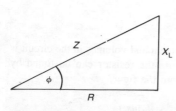

Fig. 6.15 Impedance triangle for *R* and *L* in series

The phasor sum of the two voltages V_R and V_L is equal to the applied voltage V as shown and it can be determined by measurement if the phasor diagram is drawn to scale. Alternatively, and more accurately, the magnitude V of the applied voltage can be found using

$$V = \sqrt{(V_R^2 + V_L^2)} = \sqrt{[(IR)^2 + (I\omega L)^2]} = I\sqrt{[R^2 + (\omega L)^2]}.$$

The angle ϕ between the applied voltage and the current can also be found by measurement but it is better to use

$$\phi = \tan^{-1}(\omega L/R).$$

Voltage triangle

The phasor diagram of Fig. 6.12 can be redrawn in the form of a triangle as shown in Fig. 6.13 and it is then known as the *voltage triangle*. From the triangle, $V^2 = V_R^2 + V_L^2$, $\tan \phi = V_L/V_R$, $\sin \phi = V_L/V$, and $\cos \phi = V_R/V$.

Example 6.5

The voltage $20 \sin 8000\pi t$ volts is applied across a series *LR* circuit. The resulting current lags the applied voltage by $30°$. Draw the voltage triangle and use it to determine the voltages across the inductance and across the resistance of the circuit.

Solution

The voltage triangle is shown in Fig. 6.14. The values of V_L and V_R can be found by measurement as 10 V and 17 V respectively. Alternatively, $\sin 30° = 0.5 = V_L/20$ or $V_L = 0.5 \times 20 = 10$ V; and $\cos 30° = 0.866 = V_R/20$ or $V_R = 0.866 \times 20 = 17.32$ V.   (*Ans.*)

Impedance

The *impedance Z* of a circuit is the opposition of the circuit to the flow of an a.c. current through the circuit and it is equal to the ratio (applied voltage)/current. Hence the magnitude of the impedance is

$$|Z| = \sqrt{(R^2 + X_L^2)} = \sqrt{[R^2 + (\omega L)^2]} \quad \Omega \qquad (6.4)$$

and the angle of the impedance $\angle Z$ is

$$\angle Z = \tan^{-1}(X_L/R) = \tan^{-1}(\omega L/R) \qquad (6.5)$$

Impedance triangle

The three sides of the voltage triangle each represent a voltage that is the product of a common current and an impedance. If the common current is removed from each side the impedance triangle is obtained and this is shown in Fig. 6.15. Note that no arrowheads are shown

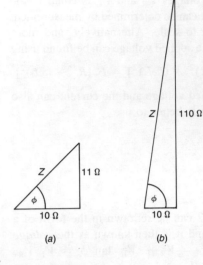

Fig. 6.16

in this triangle; this is because each of the sides of the triangle represents a quantity that is not a function of time and so has, at a particular frequency, a steady value.

From the impedance triangle, $Z^2 = R^2 + X_L^2$, $\tan \phi = X_L/R$, $\sin \phi = X_L/Z$, and $\cos \phi = R/Z$.

Example 6.6

A circuit consists of a 35 mH inductor in series with a 10 Ω resistor. Draw the impedance triangle and calculate the impedance of the circuit at (a) 50 Hz, and (b) 500 Hz.

Solution

(a) $X_L = \omega L = 2\pi \times 50 \times 35 \times 10^{-3} = 11\ \Omega$. The impedance triangle is shown in Fig. 6.16(a). From this $Z = \sqrt{(10^2 + 11^2)} = 14.87\ \Omega$ and $\phi = \tan^{-1}(11/10) = 47.7°$.

Therefore, $Z = 14.87 \angle 47.7°\ \Omega$.   (*Ans.*)

(b) $X_L = 110\ \Omega$. The impedance triangle is shown in Fig. 6.16(b) and the impedance is $Z = 110 \angle 84.8°\ \Omega$.   (*Ans.*)

Example 6.7

A resistor of 78 Ω is connected in series with a 100 mH inductor whose self-resistance is 12 Ω. The circuit is connected across a 100 V source whose frequency is 400 Hz. Calculate the impedance of the circuit. Use this to determine the current that flows in the circuit and its phase angle relative to the applied voltage.

Solution

$R = 78 + 12 = 90\ \Omega$.
$X_L = 2\pi \times 400 \times 100 \times 10^{-3} = 251.3\ \Omega$.
$Z = \sqrt{(90^2 + 251^2)} = 266.7 \simeq 277\ \Omega$.
$\angle Z = \tan^{-1}(251.3/90) = \tan^{-1} 2.79 = 70.3°$.
Therefore, $Z = 277 \angle 70.3°\ \Omega$.   (*Ans.*)
   $I = V/Z = 100/(277 \angle 70.3°) = 361 \angle -70.3°\ \text{mA}$.   (*Ans.*)

Example 6.8

Across a circuit that consists of a resistor and an inductor in series 240 volts are applied. The voltage across the inductor is 160 V and the power dissipated in the resistor is 80 W. Calculate (a) the voltage across the resistor, and (b) the current flowing in the circuit.

Solution

(a) The phasor diagram showing the current and voltages in the circuit is given in Fig. 6.17. The voltage V_R across the resistor can be found by measurement as 178 V. Alternatively, from the figure
$240 = \sqrt{(160^2 + V_R^2)}$,
$V_R = \sqrt{(240^2 - 160^2)} = 178.9\ \text{V}$.   (*Ans.*)
Or, $\sin \phi = 160/240 = 0.667$, and $\phi = 41.8°$.
$V_R = 240 \cos 41.8° = 178.9\ \text{V}$.   (*Ans.*)

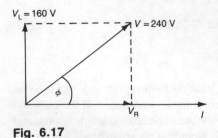

Fig. 6.17

(b) Power in resistor $R = 80\,\text{W} = I^2R = V^2/R = 178.9^2/R$
$R = 178.9^2/80 = 400\,\Omega$.
$I = V/R = 178.9/400 = 447.3\,\text{mA}$. (Ans.)

Resistance and capacitance in series

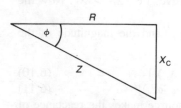

Fig. 6.18 Resistance and capacitance in series

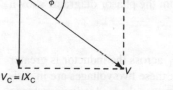

Fig. 6.19 Phasor diagram for R and C in series

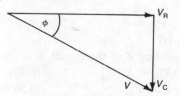

Fig. 6.20 Voltage triangle for R and C in series

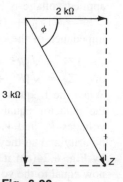

Fig. 6.21 Impedance triangle for R and C in series

The losses in a capacitor can be represented by either a small value of series resistance or a very large value of parallel resistance. In most cases the loss resistance can be neglected; if not, the series resistance alternative can be combined with the total resistance of the circuit. Figure 6.18 shows a circuit in which an a.c. voltage source is applied across a resistor and a capacitor connected in series. A current flows in the circuit equal to the applied voltage divided by the impedance of the circuit, i.e., $I = V/Z$. The current develops a voltage V_R across the resistor and a voltage V_C across the capacitor. The voltage V_R is in phase with the current and the voltage V_C lags the current by 90°. The phasor diagram for the circuit is shown by Fig. 6.19.

The applied voltage V is equal to the phasor sum of V_R and V_C, i.e., $V = \sqrt{(V_R^2 + V_C^2)} = \sqrt{[(IR)^2 + (IX_C^2)]} = I\sqrt{(R^2 + X_C^2)}$.

The voltage triangle is obtained from the phasor diagram of the circuit and it is shown in Fig. 6.20. The impedance triangle can be derived from the voltage triangle by dividing each side by the current I and it is shown in Fig. 6.21. From the figure, $Z^2 = R^2 + X_C^2$, $\tan\phi = X_C/R$, $\sin\phi = X_C/Z$, and $\cos\phi = R/Z$.

$$|Z| = \sqrt{[R^2 + (1/\omega C)^2]}\quad \Omega \qquad (6.6)$$
$$\angle Z = \tan^{-1}(1/\omega CR) \qquad (6.7)$$

Example 6.9

A capacitive reactance of 3 kΩ is connected in series with a 2 kΩ resistor and a voltage of 20 V is applied across the circuit. Calculate the current that flows and its phase angle relative to the applied voltage.

Solution

The impedance triangle for the circuit is given in Fig. 6.22. From this: $|Z| = \sqrt{(2000^2 + 3000^2)} = 3606\,\Omega$. $\angle Z = \tan^{-1}(-3/2) = -56.3°$. Therefore, $I = 20/(3606 \angle -56.3°) = 5.55 \angle 56.3°\,\text{mA}$. (Ans.)

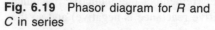

Fig. 6.22

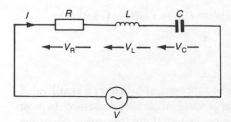

Fig. 6.23 *R, L* and *C* in series

Capacitance, inductance and resistance in series

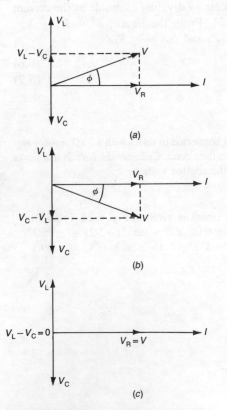

Fig. 6.24 Phasor diagrams for *R, L* and *C* in series (a) $V_L > V_C$, (b) $V_C > V_L$, and (c) $V_L = V_C$

Example 6.10

The current 20 sin (800πt) mA flows in the series connection of a 1000 Ω resistor and a 0.22 μF capacitor. Calculate (*a*) the applied voltage and its phase relative to the current, (*b*) the power dissipated in the circuit.

Solution

Reactance of capacitor $X_C = 1/(800\pi \times 0.22 \times 10^{-6}) = 1809$ Ω.
$$V_R = 20 \times 10^{-3} \times 1000 = 20 \text{ V.}$$
$$V_C = 20 \times 10^{-3} \times 1809 = 36.18 \text{ V.}$$
$$|V| = \sqrt{(20^2 + 36.18^2)} = 41.34 \text{ V.}$$
$$\phi = \tan^{-1}(-36.18/20) = -61.1°.$$
Therefore $V = 41.34 \angle -61.1°$ V.   (*Ans.*)

Figure 6.23 shows a circuit that consists of a resistor, an inductor and a capacitor connected in series and having an a.c. voltage source of *V* volts applied to it. As before, the resistance includes the self-resistances of the inductor and the capacitor. A current $I = V/Z$ flows in the circuit and develops voltages V_R, V_L and V_C across the three components. The applied voltage is equal to the phasor sum of the three voltages and this can be seen from the phasor diagrams shown in Fig. 6.24.

Three cases exist:

1. In Fig. 6.24(*a*) the voltage V_L across the inductor is greater than the capacitor voltage V_C; these two voltages are in anti-phase with one another (remember that inductive reactance is positive and capacitive reactance is negative) and so the total quadrature voltage is $V_L - V_C$. The applied voltage is, from the figure,
$$V = \sqrt{[V_R^2 + (V_L - V_C)^2]} = \sqrt{[(IR)^2 + (IX_L - IX_C)^2]}$$
The magnitude of the impedance *Z* of the circuit is
$$|Z| = V/I = \sqrt{[R^2 + (X_L - X_C)^2]} \quad (6.8)$$
$$\text{or} \quad |Z| = \sqrt{[R^2 + (\omega L - 1/\omega C)^2]} \quad (6.9)$$

2. Figure 6.24(*b*) shows the phasor diagram for the circuit of Fig. 6.23 when the frequency of the voltage source is such as to make the circuit capacitive, i.e., $X_C > X_L$. Now the applied voltage is equal to
$$V = \sqrt{[V_R^2 + (V_C - V_L)^2]}$$ and the magnitude of the impedance of the circuit is
$$|Z| = \sqrt{[R^2 + (X_C - X_L)^2]} \quad (6.10)$$
$$\text{or} \quad |Z| = \sqrt{[R^2 + (1/\omega C - \omega L)]^2} \quad (6.11)$$

3. When the frequency of the source makes the reactance of the inductor equal to the reactance of the capacitor the voltages V_L and V_C are of equal magnitude and opposite polarity and so they cancel one another out. This is shown by Fig. 6.24(*c*); it can be seen that the applied voltage is now equal to the voltage V_R across the resistor and it is also

in phase with the current. This is a condition known as *series resonance* and it is considered further on p. 110.

In all these cases $\angle Z = \tan^{-1}[(\text{effective reactance})/\text{resistance}]$.

Power in an a.c. circuit

When an a.c. current flows in a resistance the voltage developed across that resistance is in phase with the current. The average power dissipated in the resistance is then $IV = I^2R = V^2/R$ watts. An average power is not dissipated in either a pure inductance or a pure capacitance since in both cases the current is 90° out of phase with the voltage. For a circuit that contains both resistance and reactance the average power dissipated depends upon the phase angle ϕ between the current and the voltage. This fact can be demonstrated graphically and Fig. 6.25 shows two cases. In Fig. 6.25(a) the current leads the voltage by 45° and the instantaneous power curve has both positive and negative areas; the average power is clearly positive and it represents the energy supplied by the a.c. voltage source to the circuit. When the phase difference between the current and voltage waves is increased, the difference between the positive and the negative areas

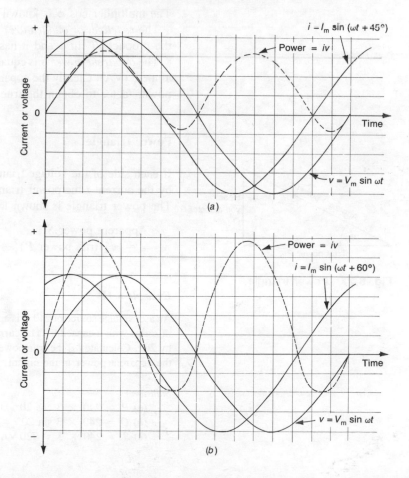

Fig. 6.25 Power in an a.c. circuit
(a) current leads voltage by 45°,
(b) current leads voltage by 60°

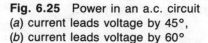

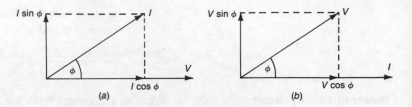

Fig. 6.26 Calculation of true power

of the instantaneous power curve becomes smaller and so therefore does the average power dissipation. This point is illustrated by Fig. 6.25(*b*) in which the current leads the voltage by 60°.

The power dissipated in a circuit can be determined by taking either the current or the voltage phasor as the reference and then resolving the other phasor into its horizontal and vertical components. Figures 6.26(*a*) and (*b*) show the two possibilities.

The *true power P* is given by the product of the 'in-phase' current and voltage or, of course, the product of the 'in-phase' voltage and current. In either case,

$$P = VI \cos \phi \qquad (6.12)$$

The multiplier cos ϕ is known as the *power factor* of the circuit.

The *reactive, or quadrature, volt-amperes Q* is the name given to the product $VI \sin \phi$ and it has the unit of var.

The *apparent power S* is equal to the product VI with the unit volt-ampere (VA). Clearly the apparent power must be multiplied by the power factor to obtain the true power.

Power triangle

If each side of the voltage triangle given in Fig. 6.13 is multiplied by the current I the power triangle for the circuit will be obtained. The power triangle is shown in Fig. 6.27. From this triangle,

$$\text{Apparent power } S \\ = \sqrt{[(\text{true power } P)^2 + (\text{reactive volt-amps } Q)^2]} \qquad (6.13)$$

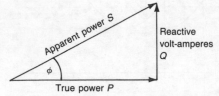

Fig. 6.27 Power triangle

Example 6.11

An a.c. voltage source of 240 V is applied to a circuit that consists of a resistor in series with a capacitor. The current that flows is 3 A leading the voltage by 20°. Calculate (*a*) the true power, (*b*) the reactive volt-amperes, and (*c*) the apparent power in the circuit.

Solution

(*a*) $P = 240 \times 3 \cos 20° = 676.6 \text{ W}.$ (*Ans.*)

(*b*) $Q = 240 \times 3 \sin 20° = 246.3 \text{ var}.$ (*Ans.*)

(*c*) $S = 240 \times 3 = 720 \text{ VA}.$ (*Ans.*)

Power factor

The power factor of a circuit is defined as:

$$\text{Power factor} = (\text{true power})/(\text{apparent power}) \qquad (6.14)$$

This relationship is always true whatever the waveforms of the current and the voltage.

If the two waveforms are sinusoidal the true power is $VI \cos \phi$ and the apparent power is VI so that the power factor is equal to $\cos \phi$ as stated earlier. When the current and the voltage waves are in phase with one another, i.e., the circuit is purely resistive, $\phi = 0°$, $\cos \phi = 1$ and the power factor is equal to unity. In a purely reactive circuit $\phi = 90°$, $\cos \phi = 0$ and so the power factor is zero. For the vast majority of a.c. circuits that possess both resistance and reactance the power factor lies somewhere in between the limits of 0 and 1.

Example 6.12

The true power in an a.c. circuit is 500 mW. If the power factor is 0.4 calculate the apparent power.

Solution

Power factor = (true power)/(apparent power).
Therefore, apparent power = $(500 \times 10^{-3})/0.4 = 1.25$ VA.   (*Ans.*)

Example 6.13

For the circuit given in Fig. 6.28 calculate (*a*) the power factor, and (*b*) the power dissipated.

Solution

The reactance X_C of the capacitor is $1/(400\pi \times 0.22 \times 10^{-6}) = 3617\,\Omega$. The phasor diagram of the circuit is shown in Fig. 6.29. From this diagram $\phi = \tan^{-1}(-3617/3000) = -50.3°$.

(*a*) Power factor = $\cos \phi = \cos 50.3° = 0.64$.   (*Ans.*)
(*b*) The impedance Z of the circuit = $\sqrt{(3000^2 + 3617^2)} = 4699\,\Omega$. The current $I_m = V_m/Z = 10/4699 = 2.13$ mA. The r.m.s. current = 1.51 mA.
Therefore, the power dissipated = $I^2R = (1.51 \times 10^{-3})^2 \times 3000$
$$= 6.84 \text{ mW.} \quad (Ans.)$$
Alternatively, $P = VI \cos \phi = 1.51 \times 10^{-3} \times 7.07 \cos 50.3°$
$$= 6.82 \text{ mW.} \quad (Ans.)$$
(The small difference in the calculated values shows the effect of rounding numbers off during a calculation.)

It is common practice to refer to a circuit as having a leading, or a lagging, power factor. This practice refers to the phase of the current relative to the voltage. A lagging power factor means that the current

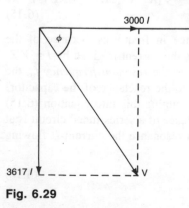

Fig. 6.28

Fig. 6.29

lags the voltage and a leading power factor means that the current leads the voltage. Thus a leading power factor of 0.342 means that the current leads the voltage by angle $\phi = \cos^{-1} 0.342 = 70°$, i.e., the circuit is capacitive.

Example 6.14

A series circuit takes a current of 1.25 A at a lagging power factor of 0.8 from a 240 V 50 Hz supply. Calculate the resistance and inductance of the circuit and draw the power triangle.

Solution

Impedance of circuit $Z = V/I = 240/1.25 = 192\,\Omega$. Power factor = $\cos \phi = R/Z$.

$R = 0.8 \times 192 = 153.6\,\Omega$.   (*Ans.*)

$X_L = \sqrt{(192^2 - 153.6^2)} = 115.2\,\Omega$,

and $L = 115.2/(2\pi \times 50) = 0.367\,\text{H}$.   (*Ans.*)

Apparent power = $VI = 240 \times 1.25 = 300\,\text{VA}$. True power = $VI \times 0.8 = 240\,\text{W}$, and reactive volt-amperes = $VI \sin \phi = 300 \sin (\cos^{-1} 0.8) = 300 \times 0.6 = 180\,\text{var}$.

The power triangle is shown in Fig. 6.30.

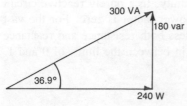

Fig. 6.30

Series resonance and Q factor

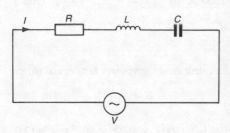

Fig. 6.31 Series-tuned circuit

A series-tuned circuit consists of an inductor and a capacitor connected in series as shown by Fig. 6.31; R represents the self-resistance of the inductor plus any actual resistor that may be included in the circuit. The capacitors employed in series-tuned circuits have negligible losses and do not contribute to the total resistance of the circuit. At any given frequency the effective reactance X_T of the circuit is the difference between the inductive reactance X_L and the capacitive reactance X_C, i.e., $X_T = X_L - X_C = \omega L - 1/\omega C$. At those frequencies making ωL greater than $1/\omega C$ the effective reactance X_T is inductive but at the lower frequencies that make $1/\omega C > \omega L$ the circuit is capacitive.

The impedance Z of the circuit is

$$Z = \sqrt{[R^2 + (X_L - X_C)^2]} = \sqrt{[R^2 + (\omega L - 1/\omega C)^2]}$$
$$= \sqrt{(R^2 + X_T^2)} \qquad (6.15)$$

The impedance varies with change in frequency because of the $(\omega L - 1/\omega C)$ term but at all times the current is given by $I = V/Z$. At a particular frequency, known as the *resonant frequency* f_o, the reactance of the inductor is equal to the reactance of the capacitor. Then $X_T = X_L - X_C = 0$. Substituting this into equation (6.15) shows that at resonance the impedance of a series-tuned circuit is at its minimum value of R ohms. At resonance the current I_o flowing in the circuit is given by

$$I_o = V/R \qquad (6.16)$$

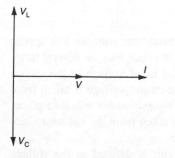

Fig. 6.32 Phasor diagram of a resonant series-tuned circuit

Since the circuit is now purely resistive the current I_o is in phase with the applied voltage and this condition in a series-tuned circuit defines series resonance. Although the effective reactance X_T is zero at resonance the reactances of the inductor and the capacitor are not themselves zero and so equal, but opposite polarity, voltages $V_L = I_o X_L$ and $V_C = I_o X_C$ are developed across the inductor and the capacitor respectively. The phasor diagram for a series-tuned circuit at resonance is shown by Fig. 6.32; the voltages V_L and V_C may be much greater than the applied voltage V. The reason for this is as follows: $I_o = V/R$, $V_L = IX_L = VX_L/R$ and $V_C = I_o X_C = VX_C/R$ and if, as is usual, R is very much smaller than both X_L and X_C the voltages appearing across the inductor and the capacitor may be much larger than the applied voltage V.

Resonant frequency

At the resonant frequency f_o the reactances of the inductor and the capacitor are equal to one another:

$$\omega_o L = 1/\omega_o C, \quad \omega_o^2 = 1/LC \text{ and } \omega_o = 1/\sqrt{LC}.$$
Hence,
$$f_o = \omega_o/2\pi = 1/2\pi\sqrt{LC} \quad \text{Hz}. \tag{6.17}$$

Example 6.15

A series-tuned circuit consists of an inductor of 10 mH and a capacitor of 4.7 nF. Calculate the resonant frequency of the circuit.

Solution
From equation (6.17),
$$f_o = 1/[2\pi \times \sqrt{(10 \times 10^{-3} \times 4.7 \times 10^{-9})}]$$
$$= 23.215 \text{ kHz}. \quad (Ans.)$$

Example 6.16

Calculate the value of capacitance that is needed to tune a 100 μH inductor to 1.34 MHz. Calculate the percentage error in the resonant frequency if the nearest preferred value of capacitance is used.

Solution
From equation (6.17),
$$C = 1/(4\pi^2 \times 1.34^2 \times 10^{12} \times 100 \times 10^{-6}) = 141 \text{ pF}. \quad (Ans.)$$
The nearest preferred value of 150 pF would have to be chosen. Using this value $f_o = 1/[2\pi \times \sqrt{(100 \times 10^{-6} \times 150 \times 10^{-12})}] = 1.2995$ MHz. The percentage error in the resonant frequency is $100(1.2995 - 1.34)/1.34 = -3.02\%$. (*Ans.*)

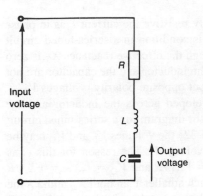

Fig. 6.33 Voltage magnification

Q factor

When a series-tuned circuit is at resonance the voltages that appear across the inductor and across the capacitance may be several times greater than the applied voltage. If the input voltage to the circuit is the voltage applied across it and the output voltage is taken from the capacitor, (see Fig. 6.33) *voltage magnification* will take place. Note that the output voltage cannot be taken from the inductor since this has inevitable inherent resistance.

The Q factor of a series-tuned circuit is defined as the voltage magnification. Thus $V_C = I_o X_C = V/\omega_o CR$ and

$$Q = V_C/V = 1/\omega_o CR \tag{6.18}$$

Since, at resonance, $\omega_o L = 1/\omega_o C$ the Q factor can also be written as

$$Q = \omega_o L/R$$

$$= (L/R)\sqrt{LC} = \frac{1}{R}\sqrt{\frac{L}{C}} \tag{6.19}$$

Equation (6.16) is also often applied to an inductor as a way of expressing its losses at any frequency $f = \omega/2\pi$ Hz, i.e., the Q factor of an inductor is $\omega L/R$.

Example 6.17

A series-tuned circuit has $L = 10$ mH, $C = 0.47$ μF and $R = 10$ Ω and has 1 V at the resonant frequency applied to it. Calculate (*a*) the resonant frequency, (*b*) the Q factor, (*c*) the voltage across the capacitor, and (*d*) the power dissipated.

Solution

(*a*) $f_o = 1/[2\pi \times \sqrt{(10 \times 10^{-3} \times 0.47 \times 10^{-6})}] = 2321$ Hz. (*Ans.*)
(*b*) $Q = \omega_o L/R = (2\pi \times 2321 \times 10 \times 10^{-3})/10 = 14.6$. (*Ans.*)
(*c*) $V_C = QV = 14.6 \times 1 = 14.6$ V. (*Ans.*)
(*d*) $I_o = V/R = 1/10 = 0.1$ A. $P = (0.1)^2 \times 10 = 100$ mW. (*Ans.*)

Example 6.18

A series-tuned circuit is resonant at 1 MHz. When 1 V at this frequency is applied across the circuit 80 V appears across the capacitor. If the total resistance of the circuit is 4.2 Ω calculate (*a*) the Q factor, (*b*) the capacitance value, (*c*) the inductance value, and (*d*) the power dissipated.

Solution

(*a*) $Q = 80/1 = 80$. (*Ans.*)
(*b*) $80 = 1/(2\pi \times 1 \times 10^6 \times 4.2 \times C)$,
$C = 473$ pF $\simeq 470$ pF. (*Ans.*)

(c) $L = 1/(4\pi^2 \times 1 \times 10^{12} \times 470 \times 10^{-12}) = 53.4\,\mu\text{H}.$ (Ans.)

(d) $I_0 = 1/4.2 = 0.238\,\text{A}.$ $P = 0.238^2 \times 4.2 = 238\,\text{mW}.$ (Ans.)

Selectivity

If the voltage of the signal applied to a series-tuned circuit is kept at a constant value and its frequency is varied the current flowing in the circuit will vary in the manner shown by Fig. 6.34. At low frequencies the circuit is capacitive $(X_C > X_L)$ and a small current flows. With increase in frequency the capacitive reactance falls and the inductive reactance increases, this causes the effective reactance X_T to fall and so the current increases. Further increase in frequency brings the circuit to its resonant condition where the current has its maximum value I_0 and is in phase with the applied voltage. Increasing the frequency above the resonant value makes the inductive reactance become larger than the capacitive reactance and so the circuit becomes inductive. Further increase in frequency increases the effective reactance of the circuit and the current falls. For particular values of L and C reducing the resistance R of the circuit gives a greater resonant current I_0 and increases the slope of the curve either side of resonance. Conversely, increasing the resistance of the circuit reduces the resonant current and produces a broader curve. The effect of the circuit resistance upon the current/frequency curve of a series-tuned circuit is shown by Fig. 6.35.

The *selectivity* of a series-tuned circuit is its ability to discriminate between signals at different frequencies. If a complex signal containing components at several different frequencies is applied to a series-tuned

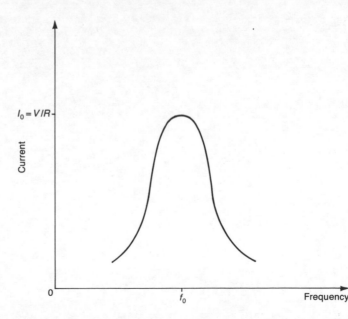

Fig. 6.34 Current–frequency curve for a series-tuned circuit

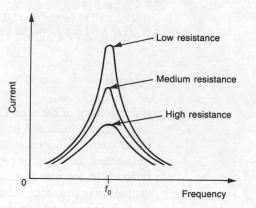

Fig. 6.35 Effect of resistance upon selectivity

circuit only those components that are at, or near, the resonant frequency will appear in the output signal at a relatively high level. The capacitor voltage varies with frequency in very nearly the same way as the current shown in Fig. 6.34. By the use of a variable capacitor a series-tuned circuit can be made to resonate at any desired frequency within a given band, and by the choice of both the *L/C* ratio and the resistance to pass only those frequencies that lie within a certain bandwidth.

7 Information transmission

A telecommunication system is employed to transmit information from one location to another by electrical means. Various systems and media are available for the transmission of the electrical signals but whichever means is employed sufficient information must arrive at the receiving end of the system for the information to be understood. In the case of analogue signals, like speech and music, the main requirement is that sufficient frequencies are retained in the received waveform for the reproduced sound to be intelligible, and for music, enjoyable also. It is also necessary that the signal-to-noise ratio* on the circuit is kept above a certain minimum figure. For data signals the waveform of the received pulses must be sufficiently well-defined for the receiver to be able accurately to determine at each instant whether binary 0 or binary 1 is being received, otherwise errors will occur.

*Signal-to-noise ratio is the ratio (wanted signal power)/(unwanted noise power).

In most cases the information that is to be transmitted over a telecommunication system is not electrical but instead consists of some other form of energy, most often either sound energy or light energy. It is therefore necessary for the information signal to be converted into an electrical signal at the transmitting end of the system by some kind of *transducer*. Transducer is the common name given to any device that is able to convert non-electrical energy into electrical energy or convert electrical energy into some form of non-electrical energy. At the distant end of the system the received electrical signal must be changed back to non-electrical form and another transducer is used to do this. Examples of transducers are many, but those commonly employed in telecommunication systems include microphones, telephone transmitters, and television cameras to convert signals into electrical form; and telephone receivers, loudspeakers, and cathode ray tubes to convert from electrical form. A microphone, or a telephone transmitter, converts incident sound energy into electrical energy and a loudspeaker or a telephone receiver converts electrical energy into sound energy. The television camera converts incident light energy into electrical energy and the cathode ray tube converts electrical energy into light energy.

The basic block diagram of a telecommunication system is shown in Fig. 7.1. The non-electrical energy produced by the information source is applied to a transducer and changed into the corresponding electrical energy. This electrical signal is passed on to the system and is then transmitted through the system to its destination. Here the electrical signal is applied to another transducer which changes the

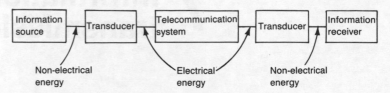

Fig. 7.1 Telecommunication system

signal into a non-electrical form that may, or may not, be the same as the original form.

The telecommunication system may be uni-directional, like sound and television broadcasting, or it may be bi-directional, as with the public switched telephone network (pstn). The system may link two fixed locations together or it may be switched (pstn), it may be routed over telephone cables, copper and/or optical fibre, over a radio link, or a combination of both cable and radio link, and it may employ either *analogue* or *digital* techniques.

Types of signal

The electrical signals handled by a telecommunication system may have several different forms. A signal may be either a *d.c. signal* or an *a.c. signal*, and it may be either an *analogue signal* or a *digital signal*. Very often a telecommunication system may not be able to transmit d.c. signals and it will then be necessary to convert the d.c. signals into a.c. form.

d.c. signals

A d.c. current is one that always flows in the same direction and a d.c. voltage is one that always has the same polarity and some examples are given on p. 67. Usually, a d.c. signal is used to operate relatively simple devices such as a bell, a lamp, or a fuel gauge. A telephone dial produces a d.c. signal; when the dial is in its rest position a steady value of d.c. current flows through the telephone and the line to the telephone exchange. When a number is dialled the dial contacts interrupt the d.c. current a number of times equal to the number dialled (0 = 10 times) and the d.c. signal thus produced operates the telephone exchange equipment; this is known as loop dialling.

For a d.c. signal to convey information it is necessary for it to be switched ON and OFF in accordance with some agreed code. Three examples of practical codes are given by Figs 7.2(*a*), (*b*) and (*c*); these show, respectively, the letter B in Morse code, in IA2 code, and in IA5 code. Figure 7.2(*a*) shows the Morse code in which a combination of *dot* and *dash* signals represent characters; a dash has a time duration three times that of a dot. The Morse code used to be commonly employed in radio communication but nowadays its use is fairly rare. Figure 7.2(*b*) uses the Murray code, also known as the

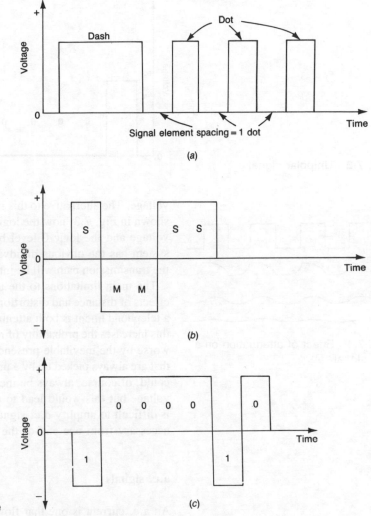

Fig. 7.2 d.c. signals, (a) Morse code, (b) IA2 code, and (c) IA5 code

International Alphabet 2 (IA2), in which all characters are of the same length and are represented by a combination of five signal elements known as *marks* and *spaces*. A mark is represented by a negative voltage, or by the presence of a tone, and a space is represented by a positive voltage, or by the absence of a tone. The IA2 code is used by teleprinters and the Telex system. Lastly, Fig. 7.2(c) shows the letter B using the ASCII code (American Standard Code for Information Interchange) or the International Alphabet 5 (IA5). It can be seen that the Murray and ASCII codes are not truly d.c. signals but since they have d.c. components (mean values) that cause problems they are usually referred to as d.c. signals.

The data signal shown in Fig. 7.2(c) consists of seven *bits* each of which may be either at binary 1 or binary 0. The waveform is said to be a double-current or bipolar signal since the logic 0 level is represented by a positive voltage and the logic 1 level by a negative

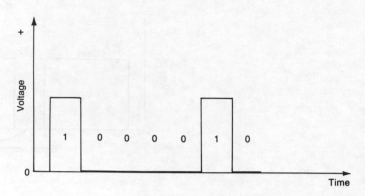

Fig. 7.3 Unipolar signal

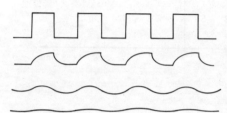

Fig. 7.4 Effect of attenuation on a d.c. signal

voltage. The alternative to this is the single-current or unipolar signal shown in Fig. 7.3; now the logic 1 level is represented by a positive voltage and the logic 0 level by the removal of that voltage. This system has the obvious disadvantage that any momentary break in the transmission path will be interpreted by the receiver as a logic 0.

The main limitations to the use of d.c. signals are the combined effects of distance and distortion. As a d.c. signal is transmitted over a telephone line it is both attenuated and distorted, see Fig. 7.4, and this increases the probability of reception errors. The situation is made worse by the inevitable presence of noise and interference voltages that are always picked up by a propagating signal. The received signal could, of course, always be increased by increasing the transmitted voltage but this would lead to other problems such as crosstalk. It is difficult to amplify d.c. signals and a continuous physical path is necessary from one end of the system to the other.

a.c. signals

An a.c. current is one that flows first in one direction and then in the other, and an a.c. voltage varies between two different polarities. Some examples of a.c. signals are given on p. 68. The use of an a.c. signal to convey information offers considerable advantages over the use of d.c. signals and a.c. signals are therefore employed in the vast majority of systems. The main advantages gained by the use of a.c. signals are:

(a) The amplitude of the signal can easily be increased by the use of amplification and/or transformer action.
(b) It is not necessary for there to be a continuous path from one end of a circuit to the other end; this allows multiplexing techniques to be employed. Multiplexing improves the efficient usage of telecommunication plant by allowing several users to transmit information simultaneously over a common transmission path.
(c) Multi-channel telephony systems can be used which allow

several circuits to be operated over a single pair of conductors giving greatly increased utilization of the transmission medium with consequent economies in plant provision.

A number of terms are used in conjunction with a.c. signals. The meanings of these terms are as follows:

Amplitude   This is the peak value of the signal. For a sinusoidal signal the positive and negative peak values are equal to one another but this is not necessarily the case for a non-sinusoidal wave.

Complex   A complex signal is one which contains components at two or more different frequencies. The lowest frequency is called the *fundamental frequency* and all the other frequencies, which are at integer multiples of the fundamental frequency, are known as *harmonics*. This means that a complex signal must have a non-sinusoidal waveform.

Frequency   The frequency f of an a.c. signal is the number of complete cycles that occur in one second.

Period   The period, or the periodic time, of an a.c. signal is the time occupied by one cycle of the waveform. The periodic time is equal to the reciprocal of the frequency of the signal.

Example 7.1

A complex signal contains components at the following frequencies: 500 Hz, 1500 Hz, 2000 Hz, 3000 Hz, 3500 Hz and 4000 Hz. State which frequency is (a) the fundamental, (b) the fourth harmonic, and (c) the seventh harmonic.

Solution

(a) The fundamental is the lowest frequency, i.e., 500 Hz.   (*Ans.*)
(b) The fourth harmonic is $4 \times 500 = 2000$ Hz.   (*Ans.*)
(c) The seventh harmonic is $7 \times 500 = 3500$ Hz.   (*Ans.*)

Analogue signals

An analogue signal is one whose amplitude and/or frequency varies continuously with time and may have any value in between pre-set limits. An analogue signal will change very little from one instant to the next and a typical example of an analogue signal is shown by Fig. 7.5. Neglecting any distortion that may be present the waveform of the analogue signal will be a replica of the waveform of the information signal. Many electronic equipments are designed to work with analogue signals and two examples, found in most homes, are the domestic radio receiver and the television receiver.

Most transducers generate an analogue output signal. The telephone receiver is a device which incorporates a ferromagnetic diaphragm that is caused to vibrate whenever an a.c. current flows through the receiver's windings. The vibrating diaphragm produces sound waves

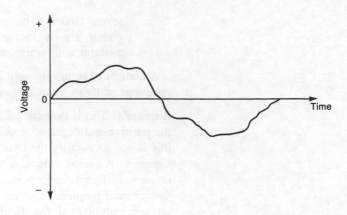

Fig. 7.5 Analogue signal

that have the same waveform as the current. The telephone transmitter is a device whose electrical resistance is varied by any incident sound wave. Consider Fig. 7.6. When no sound is incident upon the transmitter only the normal atmospheric pressure is exerted upon the device and then its electrical resistance is at its mean value and a steady d.c. current flows to line. When someone speaks into the transmitter the air pressure is alternately increased and decreased, or compressed and rarefied, with a waveform that depends upon the nature of the speech. Figure 7.6(a) shows the assumed waveform. When the pressure on the transmitter is increased the resistance of the transmitter is decreased; conversely the transmitter resistance is increased whenever the air pressure is reduced. This is shown by Fig. 7.6(b). Since the voltage applied across the transmitter is constant a decrease in the resistance of the transmitter results in an increase in the current flowing through it and vice versa; this is shown by Fig. 7.6(c). It can be seen that the current waveform is in phase with the sound waveform and is identical to it (assuming zero distortion). The analogue signal thus generated is sent into the telecommunication system and transmitted through it to arrive eventually at the distant telephone receiver. Here the current waveform passes through the telephone receiver and causes its diaphragm to vibrate and these vibrations produce the original speech waveform.

In practice, both the telephone transmitter and the telephone receiver do not have uniform output/frequency characteristics and so some distortion is always present.

As the analogue signal is transmitted through an analogue telecommunication system, be it line or radio, it will be attenuated and will pick up noise and so its signal-to-noise ratio will fall. The signal-to-noise ratio cannot be improved by amplifying the signal because both the signal and the noise will be amplified to the same extent and, in addition, each amplifier will introduce further noise of its own. This means that the signal-to-noise ratio on an analogue circuit inevitably falls with increase in the length of the circuit. The signal-to-noise ratio must never be allowed to fall below the minimum figure required for that kind of signal.

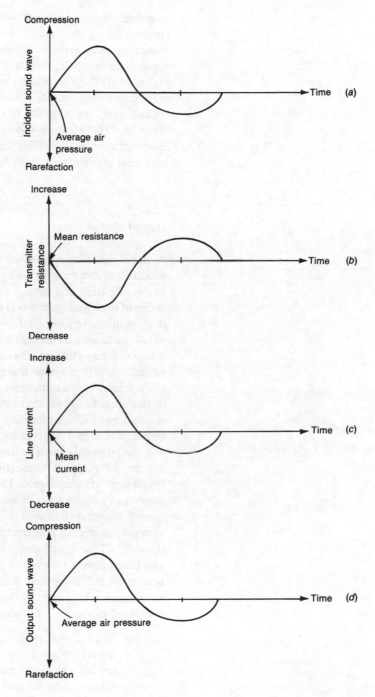

Fig. 7.6 Operation of a telephone transmitter

Frequencies and bandwidths

When a person speaks the sound waves produced contain components at frequencies in the band 100–10 000 Hz. The pitch of the speech is determined by the fundamental frequency and the loudness by the amplitude of the speech waveform. The notes produced by a musical instrument occupy a much wider bandwidth than does speech and frequencies in the range 50−15 000 Hz may be generated. The frequency range over which the average human ear can respond is approximately 30−16 500 Hz with the greatest sensitivity being in the region of 1000−2000 Hz. By international agreement the bandwidth for a 'commercial-quality' speech circuit is 300−3400 Hz, but circuits routed over some radio links may have a bandwidth of just 300−3000 Hz. Medium-wave sound broadcast signals have an audio bandwidth of 50−4500 Hz and frequency-modulated vhf sound broadcast signals have an audio bandwidth of 15 kHz.

Digital signals

A digital signal is not continuous but consists of discrete voltage pulses which represent the information signal. A digital signal can only vary in discrete steps and usually only two voltage levels are employed. If one of these voltage levels is 0 V the electronic circuitry can employ devices that have just two stable states, either ON or OFF. Examples of *two-state devices* are: (*a*) a lamp that is either glowing visibly or it is not; (*b*) a switch which is either closed or open; and (*c*) a buzzer or bell, which is either making an audible noise or it is not. In electronic circuitry transistors, bipolar or field effect, and less often diodes are used as two-state devices; in operation they are either fully conducting or ON, or they are non-conducting or OFF. An example of a digital signal is given by Fig. 7.2(*c*).

A digital signal cannot be transmitted over an analogue transmission system without first converting the digital signal to be a voice-frequency (vf) a.c. signal. Digital transmission systems possess a number of advantages over analogue transmission systems and in the United Kingdom British Telecom are converting line transmission systems from analogue working to digital operation as rapidly as possible. The eventual aim is to have an integrated digital switching and transmission system covering the entire country; this will be known as the Integrated Services Digital Network (ISDN). The advantages to be gained by the use of digital transmission techniques compared to the use of analogue techniques are:

(*a*) Since digital pulses can always be regenerated at regular intervals along a line the signal-to-noise ratio on the line need not fall with distance as is inevitably the case with an analogue system. Any desired value of signal-to-noise ratio can be obtained at the receiving end of a system.
(*b*) Improved signalling.
(*c*) Multiplexing is easier using *digital time-division multiplex* (tdm) than using analogue frequency-division multiplex (fdm). There are two reasons for this: (i) the use of pulse regenerators provides an almost distortion-free transmission

path regardless of distance, and (ii) channel selection is achieved by means of inexpensive channel gates rather than expensive filters.

(*d*) Digital switching is easier to implement than is analogue switching.

(*e*) Different kinds of signal, i.e., data, telegraph, speech and television can be treated as identical signals during transmission and switching.

The main disadvantage of digital operation is the wider bandwidth that is necessary. There used to be another disadvantage that delayed the introduction of digital transmission for many years; this was that the sheer complexity of much of the circuitry needed made it uneconomic but now the widespread introduction of large-scale integration (lsi) and very-large-scale integration (vlsi) integrated circuits (ICs) has overcome this difficulty.

Velocity and wavelength

The propagation of an a.c. current, or voltage, along a transmission line, or of a radio wave through the atmosphere, does not happen instantaneously but takes a finite length of time. This means that there is always a time lag between the application of a signal to the sending-end of a line and its reception at the other end. Hence there is always a phase difference between the a.c. voltage at the sending end of a line and the a.c. voltage at any point along the line at a given instant. If, for example, the voltage one kilometre from the sending end of a line lags the sending-end voltage by 30° then at a distance of two kilometres the voltage will lag the sending-end voltage by 2 × 30° = 60°. Three kilometres down the line the voltage will lag by 90° and so on for each kilometre along the line. The voltage 12 km along the line will be in phase with the sending-end voltage because 12 × 30° = 360° = 0°. For this line 12 km is the *wavelength* λ of the signal.

The wavelength λ of a signal is the distance between two adjacent points at which the instantaneous phase is the same, e.g., two positive peaks, or two negative peaks, or two zeros with the signal about to go positive; these are shown by Fig. 7.7.

A sinusoidal wave of frequency *f* has a periodic time *T* equal to $1/f$ seconds. In this time the wave will travel a distance equal to *T* times the velocity *v* with which the wave is propagated, and the sending-end voltage will have passed through one complete cycle of instantaneous values. Therefore,

$$\lambda = vT = v/f, \quad \text{or} \quad v = f\lambda. \tag{7.1}$$

A radio wave travels through the atmosphere with a velocity equal to the velocity of light, i.e. 3×10^8 m/s. A current, or voltage, wave travels along a transmission line with a velocity that may be very much less than this in some cases or very nearly equal to it in other cases.

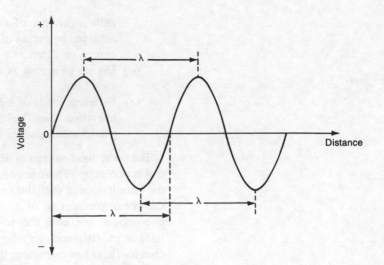

Fig. 7.7 Wavelength of a signal

Example 7.2

A 50 MHz radio wave is propagated through the atmosphere. Calculate its wavelength.

Solution
$$\lambda = (3 \times 10^8)/(50 \times 10^6) = 6\,\text{m}. \quad (Ans.)$$

Example 7.3

Two radio stations operate at frequencies that are 18 kHz apart. If the lower-frequency station operates at 1 MHz express their separation in wavelengths.

Solution
For the lower-frequency station $\lambda = (3 \times 10^8)/(1 \times 10^6) = 300\,\text{m}$.
For the other station $\lambda = (3 \times 10^8)/(1.018 \times 10^6) = 294.696\,\text{m}$.
Therefore, the wavelength separation $= 5.304\,\text{m}$. (*Ans.*)

Modulation

The analogue signal waveform produced by speech or music cannot be directly radiated from an aerial since radiation only takes place at frequencies higher than about 10 kHz. It is therefore necessary for each signal to be *frequency translated* or *shifted* to a higher radio frequency. To make it possible for a radio receiver to select the wanted signal from all those signals simultaneously present at its aerial, it is also necessary for different radio stations within a given geographical area to operate at different frequencies. To position the various radio stations at different parts of the radio frequency spectrum the information signal must *modulate* a sinusoidal *carrier wave*. The frequency of the carrier wave must be chosen to be the frequency to which the information or *modulating* signal is to be shifted. The modulating signal may modulate either the amplitude or the frequency of the carrier wave; the former gives *amplitude modulation* and the latter gives *frequency modulation*.

Modulation is also employed to increase the channel-carrying capacity of a telephone line. A number of channels can each modulate a different carrier frequency so that the channels are positioned side by side in the frequency spectrum provided by the line. This is a technique that is known as *frequency-division multiplex* (fdm); it is no longer employed in the telephone network of the UK for multi-channel telephony systems since these have all been replaced by *pulse-code modulation systems*. Frequency-division multiplex is, however, still employed for some data communication systems and by some microwave radio-relay systems.

The data signal produced by a computer, or by a data terminal, is either a unipolar or a bipolar d.c. signal. Such a signal can be transmitted over short-distance lines, over digital services such as British Telecom's Kilostream and Megastream, and over a *local area network* (LAN). A d.c. data signal cannot, however, be transmitted over the analogue telephone network. There are several reasons for this:

(a) The resistance and capacitance of the line combine to distort the received waveform to such an extent that the receiver cannot reliably decide whether a logic 1 or logic 0 pulse is being received at any particular instant in time.

(b) Line transformers, amplifiers, and transmission bridges in telephone exchange equipment, will remove the d.c component (the average value) from the signal.

(c) All but the shortest links are routed over one, or more, multi-channel pulse-code modulated (pcm) telephony systems and/or a radio link and these systems do not pass frequencies below 300 Hz.

Removal of the d.c. component from a d.c. data signal has the effect of shifting the data waveform relative to the 0 V axis and thereby increases the probability of an error in the receipt of the data. The effect of removing the d.c. component is illustrated by Fig. 7.8. The d.c. component of the transmitted waveform shown in Fig. 7.8(a) is $-(6/7) \times 3 = -2.57$ V. If this d.c. component is removed from the data waveform the resulting waveform will vary from a maximum value of $+6 - (-2.57) = +8.57$ V, and a minimum value of $-6 - (-2.57) = -3.43$ V as shown by Fig. 7.8(b). The effects of line attenuation, noise and distortion will soon ensure that the receiver is unable reliably to detect the presence of the binary 1 pulses.

When a d.c data signal is to be transmitted over an analogue telecommunication system it must first be converted into *voice-frequency* (vf) form by an equipment known as a modem. A modem is able to convert signals from digital form to vf form in one direction of transmission, and in the reverse direction convert signals from vf form to digital form. The vf data signal can then be transmitted over

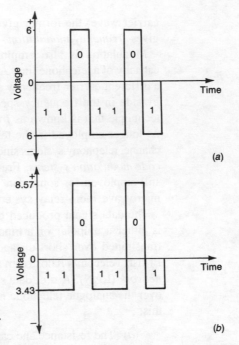

Fig. 7.8 Effect of removing the d.c. component from a digital signal

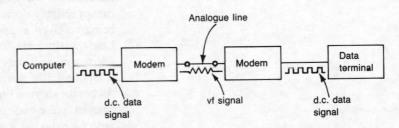

Fig. 7.9 Use of a modem

the analogue system in the same way as a speech signal. At the distant end of the circuit another modem is used to convert the vf data signal back into its original digital form. Figure 7.9 shows a simple point-to-point data circuit that uses a modem at each end to convert data signals from d.c. form into vf form and vice versa. In the transmitting modem the d.c. data signal modulates a carrier to position the vf signal somewhere in the bandwidth 750–2850 Hz.

Amplitude modulation

Amplitude modulation is the process of varying the amplitude V_c of a sinusoidal carrier wave in accordance with the instantaneous value of a modulating signal. The amplitude is varied by an amount that is directly proportional to the amplitude V_m of the modulating signal, and it is varied a number of times per second that is equal to the frequency of the modulating signal.

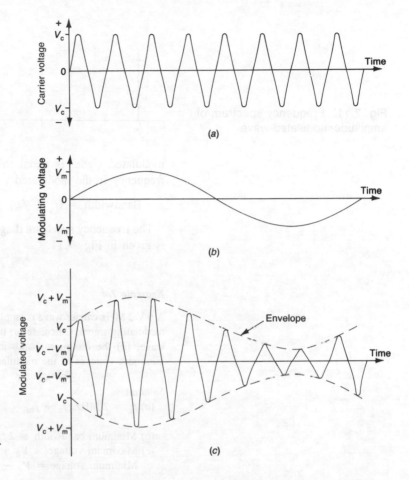

Fig. 7.10 (a) carrier signal, (b) modulating signal, and (c) amplitude-modulated wave

Figure 7.10(c) shows the waveform produced when the carrier wave of Fig. 7.10(a), of frequency f_c, is amplitude modulated by the sinusoidal modulating signal, of frequency f_m, shown in Fig. 7.10(b). The carrier frequency has been shown at a frequency of only eight times the modulating signal frequency but it would, in practice, usually be much greater than this. The following points should be noted about an amplitude modulated wave:

(a) The peak value, or amplitude, of the modulated waveform varies between a maximum value of $\pm (V_c + V_m)$ and a minimum value of $\pm (V_c - V_m)$ volts.

(b) The outline of the modulated waveform, shown dotted, is known as the *modulation envelope*.

(c) The modulated wave contains components at the following frequencies: (i) the carrier frequency f_c, (ii) the *lower side-frequency* $f_c - f_m$, and (iii) the *upper side-frequency* $f_c + f_m$. The modulating signal itself is *not* present in the modulated wave. This means that the process of amplitude modulation has shifted the modulating signal from its original frequency to both a lower, and a higher, side-frequency. The minimum bandwidth necessary to transmit the

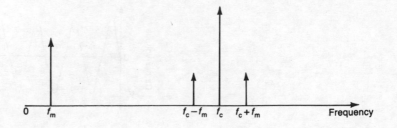

Fig. 7.11 Frequency spectrum of amplitude-modulated wave

modulated signal is equal to the difference between the highest frequency in the modulated wave and the lowest frequency, i.e.,

$$\text{Bandwidth} = (f_c + f_m) - (f_c - f_m) = 2f_m. \qquad (7.2)$$

The frequency spectrum diagram of the amplitude-modulated wave is given in Fig. 7.11.

Example 7.4

A 6 V 2 MHz carrier wave is amplitude modulated by a 2 V 4 kHz sinusoidal modulating signal. Calculate (*a*) the frequencies contained in the modulated wave, (*b*) the minimum bandwidth required, and (*c*) the maximum and minimum voltages of the modulated wave.

Solution

(*a*) $f_c = 2\,\text{MHz}$, $f_c + f_m = 2.004\,\text{MHz}$, and $f_c - f_m = 1.996\,\text{MHz}$.
(*Ans.*)

(*b*) Minimum bandwidth $= 2f_m = 8\,\text{kHz}$. (*Ans.*)

(*c*) Maximum voltage $= V_c + V_m = 6 + 2 = 8\,\text{V}$. (*Ans.*)
Minimum voltage $= V_c - V_m = 6 - 2 = 4\,\text{V}$. (*Ans.*)

Sidebands

When a complex signal that contains components at two or more frequencies amplitude modulates a sinusoidal carrier wave, each frequency in the modulating signal will produce corresponding lower, and upper, side-frequencies. Suppose that the lowest frequency in the modulating signal is f_1 and the highest frequency is f_2. Then f_1 will produce a lower side-frequency of $f_c - f_1$ and an upper side-frequency of $f_c + f_1$, while f_2 will produce a lower side-frequency at $f_c - f_2$ and an upper side-frequency $f_c + f_2$. The modulating signal will therefore produce a number of lower side-frequency components lying in the band $(f_c - f_2)$ to $(f_c - f_1)$ and this band of frequencies is known as the *lower sideband*. Similarly, an *upper sideband* containing components at frequencies from $(f_c + f_1)$ to $(f_c + f_2)$ is also produced.

Example 7.5

A 100 kHz carrier is amplitude modulated by the band of frequencies 300–3400 Hz. Calculate the frequencies contained in the modulated waveform

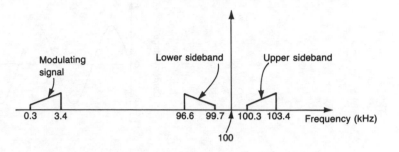

Fig. 7.12

and draw the spectrum diagram. What bandwidth is needed to transmit the modulated signal?

Solution
The frequencies contained in modulated wave are (i) $f_c = 100$ kHz, (ii) lower sideband: $100\,000 - 3400$ Hz to $100\,000 - 300$ Hz or 96.6 to 99.7 kHz, (iii) upper sideband: $100\,000 + 300$ Hz to $100\,000 + 3400$ Hz or 100.3 to 103.4 kHz.   (*Ans.*)
The spectrum diagram is shown in Fig. 7.12. The modulating signal and the two sidebands are represented by truncated triangles in which the vertical ordinates are made proportional to the *modulating frequency* and no account is taken of amplitude.
The necessary bandwidth is $103.4 - 96.6 = 6.8$ kHz.   (*Ans.*)
Note that this bandwidth is equal to *twice* the highest frequency in the complex modulating signal.

Frequency modulation

When a sinusoidal carrier wave is frequency modulated its amplitude is kept constant and its frequency is made to vary in accordance with the instantaneous voltage of the modulating signal. The amount by which the carrier frequency is deviated from its unmodulated value, known as the frequency deviation, is proportional to the amplitude of the modulating signal and the number of times per second this frequency deviation occurs is equal to the modulating signal frequency. Frequency modulation of a carrier is illustrated by Fig. 7.13. The unmodulated carrier wave, Fig. 7.13(*a*), is of constant amplitude and phase and the modulating signal, Fig. 7.13(*b*), is of sinusoidal waveform.

The frequency-modulated waveform is shown in Fig. 7.13(*c*); it can be seen that the frequency of the wave increases above its unmodulated value for a time period equal to one-quarter the periodic time T of the modulating signal. The maximum frequency is reached after time $T/4$ and then in the time period $T/4$ to $T/2$ the frequency decreases until it reaches its unmodulated value at time $t = T/2$. In the time period $T/2$ to T the frequency of the wave becomes less than its unmodulated value, reaching its minimum value at time $t = 3T/4$.

The number of side-frequencies contained in the sinusoidally modulated carrier wave depends upon both the amplitude and the

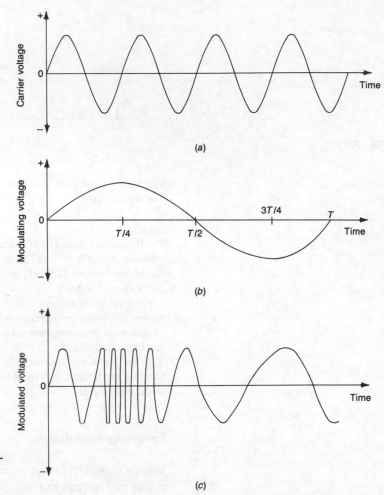

Fig. 7.13 (a) Carrier signal, (b) modulating signal, and (c) frequency-modulated wave

frequency of the modulating signal. A narrow-band frequency-modulated (nbfm) wave, such as is used in a land mobile radio system, may only contain the same frequencies as an amplitude-modulated wave, i.e., the carrier frequency f_c, and the upper and lower side-frequencies $f_c \pm f_m$. Wideband frequency-modulated systems, such as vhf sound broadcasts, the sound signal for uhf television, and microwave radio relay systems, contain components at the carrier frequency f_c, the first-order side-frequencies $f_c \pm f_m$, the second-order side-frequencies $f_c \pm 2f_m$, the third-order side-frequencies $f_c \pm 3f_m$, etc. up to the nth-order side-frequencies $f_c \pm nf_m$. When a carrier is frequency modulated by a complex signal the number of side-frequencies generated may be very large indeed.

Frequency shift modulation

Modems that work at bit rates of 300, 600 and 1200 bits/s employ frequency shift modulation (fsk) to convert the d.c. data signal into the corresponding vf signal. The carrier frequency is *always* deviated

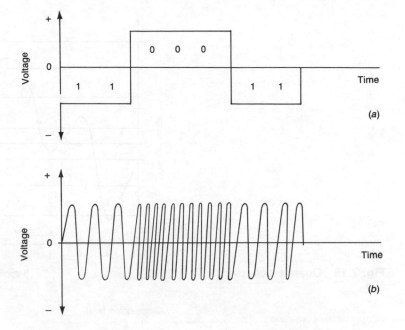

Fig. 7.14 Frequency shift modulation

to one, or other, of two different frequencies; the higher frequency is used to represent binary 0 while the lower frequency represents binary 1. An example of a d.c. data signal is given in Fig. 7.14(*a*) and the corresponding fsk vf signal is shown by Fig. 7.14(*b*).

At higher bit rates two other forms of digital modulation, known as differential phase shift modulation (dpsk) and quadrature amplitude modulation (qam) are employed.

Pulse code modulation

Pulse code modulation (pcm) is a digital transmission technique that is based upon the sampling of the amplitude of the information signal at regular intervals of time. Information about each sample is then transmitted, using the binary code and digital transmission, over a suitable transmission line.

The total audio-frequency amplitude range that the system is able to transmit is divided into a number of *quantization levels*. Each quantization level is allocated a number as shown by Fig. 7.15 in which eight levels have been drawn. The analogue information signal is sampled at regular intervals, labelled 1 through to 9, to produce a *pulse amplitude modulated* (pam) waveform as shown in Fig. 7.16. The pam waveform is then applied to an *encoder* in which the amplitudes of the pulses are rounded off to the nearest quantization level. Thus, referring to Fig. 7.16, the pam pulses are rounded off to, in turn, 3, 1, 4, 3, 5, 6, 5, 0, and 1. The value of each quantization level is then encoded into the equivalent binary number and is then transmitted to line. When the basic binary code is employed a voltage pulse is sent to line to indicate binary 1 and no pulse is sent to indicate binary 0; the pulses are all of constant height and width and the pulse

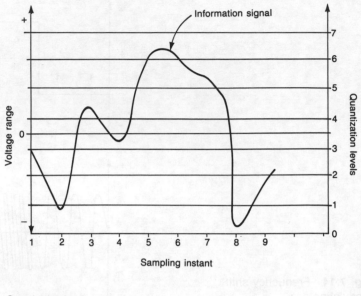

Fig. 7.15 Quantization levels

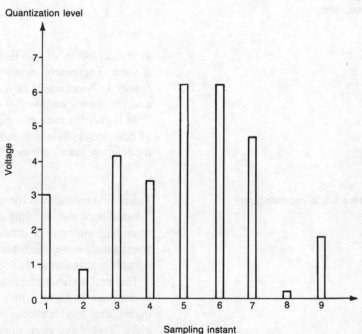

Fig. 7.16 pam waveform

train that represents the signal given in Fig. 7.15 is shown by Fig. 7.17. A space, equal in time duration to one bit, has been left between each binary number. For various reasons this basic pulse train is usually further encoded to give a more complex signal.

The number of quantization levels employed is always some multiple of two; in Fig. 7.15 only eight levels have been used to clarify the drawing but in the CCITT 30-channel pcm system there are 256 levels and so eight bits are needed to represent each level, since $2^8 = 256$.

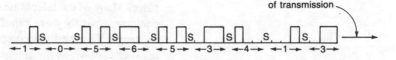

Fig. 7.17 pcm waveform

Time division multiplex

The information signal must be sampled a sufficient number of times per second for the waveform at the receiver to be correctly reconstituted. The minimum sampling frequency that is necessary is equal to twice the highest frequency contained in the information signal. For the commercial-quality speech bandwidth this is 6.8 kHz but the CCITT recommend that a sampling frequency of 8 kHz is employed. Each sample is signalled to line by eight bits and occupies a *time slot* of 3.9 μs. Samples are taken every 1/8000 s or 125 μs so that the larger part of each sampling period is unoccupied. The unused time can be employed to carry other pcm channels; the number of channels that can be transmitted in the available time is 125/3.9 = 32. When the pcm system is used to carry speech signals two of the channels are used for synchronization and signalling purposes so that 30 channels are available. When the system is used to carry data signals, e.g., British Telecom's Kilostream service, all 32 channels can be used.

Systems and media

Information signals may be transmitted from one point to another by various electrical means. The main kinds of system employed are telephony, telegraphy, radio, television, and data communication. Local circuits in the public switched telephone system (pstn) are routed over unit twin copper conductors in multi-pair cables. Longer-distance circuits are nearly all routed via 30-channel pcm systems that, in turn, use either copper conductors in star-quad or coaxial cables, or optical fibre cable. Multi-channel systems are used in order to gain the utmost utilization of the bandwidth of the transmission medium. Optical fibre cables offer the following advantages over copper conductor cables:

(*a*) light-weight, small dimensioned cables;
(*b*) very wide bandwidth;
(*c*) freedom from electro-magnetic interference;
(*d*) low losses;
(*e*) high reliability and long life;
(*f*) cheap and readily available raw materials;
(*g*) negligible crosstalk between fibres in the same cable.

Optical fibre cables are particularly suited to the transmission of digital signals.

The reasons for using the public telephone service are well known. A connection can be set up with another telephone situated at any location in the whole world and then a real-time conversation can take place. Many of the telephone exchanges in the UK still use analogue equipment but they are rapidly being replaced by digital telephone exchanges. Eventually, a completely digital transmission and switching network, known as the Integrated Service Digital Network (ISDN), will exist and then the pstn will offer many extra services in addition to those presently available.

Telegraphy offers an advantage over telephony in that it provides a printed record of the information which has been sent and received. The pstn is not suited to the transmission of telegraph signals and a separate *Telex* network is in existence. The Telex network operates in a similar way to the pstn to inter-connect teleprinters. Another form of telegraphy which has become of considerable commercial importance in recent years is known as facsimile telegraphy or FAX. FAX is the transmission of photographs, diagrams, documents, etc., by electrical means and it operates over the pstn.

Sound and television broadcast systems are well known and provide information and entertainment to anyone who has access to a radio, or a television receiver. Communication is one-way only and so no interaction is possible. The medium employed is radio propagation between the radio/television transmitter and the radio/television receiver, but some use of cable is made at both ends. Radio transmission is also important for many other forms of communication. Many long-distance telephone circuits are routed over microwave radio-relay links which may be either terrestrial or via a communication satellite. Both analogue and digital radio-relay systems are in use.

The choice of transmission system for a particular route is based upon a careful consideration of all the relevant factors, such as the required transmission performance, the economics involved, and the nature of the terrain to be covered. The relative merits of cable and radio-relay systems are as follows:

(*a*) A radio-relay system is generally easier and quicker to provide.
(*b*) The problems posed by difficult terrain are more easily overcome when radio-relay is used.
(*c*) It is easier to extend the traffic-carrying capacity of a radio-relay system.
(*d*) Difficulties may be experienced in obtaining suitable sites for radio-relay terminals.
(*e*) The performance of a radio-relay system may be affected by bad weather conditions.

In the UK the national telephone network employs digital pcm systems routed over a mixture of copper and fibre optic cable, and radio-relay links. Submarine cables and communication satellites provide international communications between the UK and other countries.

Data communications

The term 'data' means information that is represented by a binary electrical signal. Data communication is the transmission of data between two computers, or between a computer and either a peripheral or a data terminal. The computer may be a main-frame or host computer, a mini-computer, or a micro-computer (personal or home). A wide variety of peripherals and data terminals are employed including disc drives, printers, visual display units (VDUs), and modems.

Many firms and organizations have installed their own data networks to transfer data from one location to another, to calculate wages and salaries, to produce bills, invoices, receipts, etc. Other applications include the booking of package holidays, aeroplane seats, theatre seats, etc., the checking of credit card validity, electronic fund transfer, and bank/building society wall cash dispensers.

Serial and parallel transmission of data

In a data communication system characters must be sent from one point to another; the characters must be coded before transmission and the most commonly employed code is the International Alphabet No. 5 (IA5) which is also known as the ASCII* code. With this code eight bits are used per character; seven bits represent the character and the eighth bit is a *parity* bit that is used for error detection purposes. The eight bits are known as a *byte*. Data can be transmitted between a computer and a peripheral, a terminal or a modem using either serial or parallel transmission.

*ASCII: American Standard Code For Information Interchange.

Parallel transmission

When parallel transmission of data is used all the eight bits comprising a character are sent simultaneously over eight separate conductors as shown by Fig. 7.18. In practice, some extra conductors would be needed to allow *handshaking* between the computer and the peripheral to be carried out. Handshaking is a procedure that allows the two parties to a data transfer to communicate satisfactorily even though they may operate at different speeds. The number of conductors needed in a parallel interface is known as the *bus width*. Because several conductors are necessary to transmit the data, parallel transmission is only an economic proposition over fairly short distances. Parallel data transmission gives a very fast data transfer and it is used between a computer and nearby printers, disc drives, and other peripherals.

Serial transmission

Serial transmission of data is employed for all but the very shortest computer-to-peripheral connections and its basic concept is

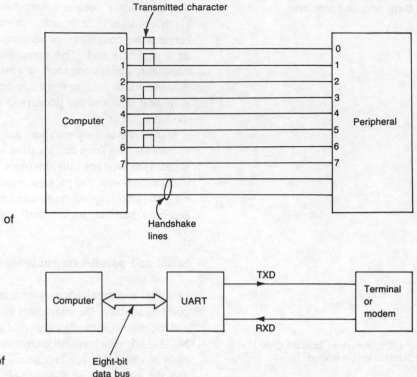

Fig. 7.18 Parallel transmission of data

Fig. 7.19 Serial transmission of data

illustrated by Fig. 7.19. The data to and from the computer is passed over an eight-bit data bus to a device known variously as UART, an ACIA etc. The UART, etc., is an IC which in one direction of transmission converts data from parallel form into serial form, and in the other direction of transmission converts data from serial form into parallel form. The parallel data, transmitted by the computer, enters the UART and is changed into serial form and then it is sent over the single 'transmit data' (TXD) conductor to the terminal or modem. The least significant bit is transmitted first, the most significant bit is transmitted last but one, and the parity bit is transmitted last. Since the bits forming each character are transmitted one after the other and not simultaneously the *data transfer rate* is much less than for parallel transmission. At the other end of the circuit the receiver must sample the incoming data bits at the correct instants in time before it can reproduce the received characters correctly. If the data is sent to a modem it is here changed into the corresponding vf signal before it is transmitted over the telephone line. In the opposite direction the terminal, or the modem, transmits serial data to the UART over the 'received data line' (RXD). The received data is converted into parallel form by the UART and it is then passed on to the computer.

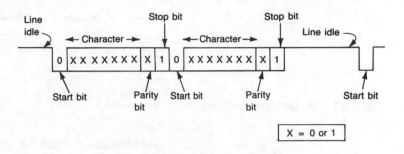

Fig. 7.20 Non-synchronous data signal

X = 0 or 1

Non-synchronous data transmission

When data is transmitted non-synchronously each character is sent as a completely separate entity. The time between the last bit of one character and the first bit of the next character is not fixed. The receiver must sample the incoming bits at the correct instants in time and its timing is controlled by a *clock*. The clock is generated locally within the receiver and it is kept in synchronism with the transmitter clock by the use of start and stop bits that are transmitted with every character. When the line is idle a voltage at the binary 1 level is applied to the line and this stops the receiver clock. When a transmitter has data to send it switches the line voltage to the binary 0 level for a 1-bit period of time; this is known as the *start bit*. The clock in the receiver is started by the change from 1 to 0 of the leading edge of the start bit and it then runs freely to generate clock pulses. At the end of each character a *stop bit*, which is at the binary 1 voltage level, stops the receiver clock. The receiver clock then waits until the next start bit is received. Synchronization between the clocks in the transmitter and in the receiver is therefore carried out on a character-by-character basis and so the receiver clock need not be very stable. Figure 7.20 shows the waveform of a data signal that uses start—stop synchronization.

Synchronous data transmission

Start and stop bits are not employed when synchronous data transmission is used. The clock in the receiver runs continuously and it must be kept in synchronism with the clock in the transmitter. To achieve this, clocking information must be transmitted over the circuit along with the data. Bytes of data are continuously transmitted without any gaps for as long as is necessary to pass the message. If any gaps do occur in the data stream they are filled by padding bytes. Figure 7.21 shows a synchronous data stream.

The receiver must start sampling the incoming data at the middle of the first bit of the first character received. This is known as *bit*

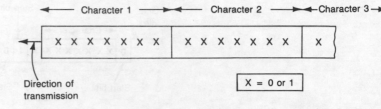

Fig. 7.21 Synchronous data signal

synchronization. Once bit synchronization has been achieved the receiver must then decide which group of bits constitutes a character; this is known as *character synchronization*. To do this the receiver monitors the incoming data on a bit-by-bit basis until it recognizes a character synchronization pattern. Then the receiver is able to determine which set of received bits make up the first character to be received. Subsequent characters can then be recognized correctly. The need for synchronization means that some form of *protocol* is necessary.

Relative merits of non-synchronous and synchronous transmission

Non-synchronous transmission of data is relatively simple and cheap. The data bytes that arrive at the receiver are separated by start and stop bits making it easy to achieve character synchronization. Since the receiver clock is stopped and then re-started after each received character the clock only needs to remain in synchronism for an eight-bit time period. A relatively simple clock is therefore adequate and bit synchronization is not a problem. Non-synchronous transmission of data is only suitable for low bit rates because (*a*) the use of start and stop bits means that two bits in every ten carry no information and the maximum data transfer rate is reduced, and (*b*) a free-running clock only gives a satisfactory performance at low bit rates.

Synchronous transmission of data is more expensive but it can operate at much higher bit rates and has a higher data transfer efficiency because there are no start or stop bits.

Non-synchronous transmission is used for teleprinter-compatible terminals, for 'within-house' terminal-to-terminal communication, and for communication over the pstn at the lower bit rates. Synchronous transmission is used by many VDUs, by remote job-entry batch terminals, in host computer networks, and for the higher bit rates over the pstn.

Protocols

A protocol is a set of rules by which two stations, computers and/or terminals, may transfer data between them in a number of blocks or

Table 7.1

Pin No.	CCITT No.	CCITT V24 Name	RS 232C RS 232C label	Direction
1	101	earth	AA	–
2	103	transmitted data (TXD)	BA	T > M
3	104	received data (RXD)	BB	M > T
4	105	request to send (RTS)	CA	T > M
5	106	clear to send (CTS)	CB	M > T
6	107	data set ready (DSR)	CC	M > T
7	102	common signal return	AB	–
8	109	data channel received signal detector (CD)	CF	M > T
20	108/1	connect data set to line		
or	108/2	data terminal ready (DTR)	CD	T > M
22	125	calling indicator (CI) (ring indicator (RI) in RS 232C)	CE	M > T

frames. A protocol caters for the synchronization of the receiver clock, the detection of errors, and for the maintenance of data flow. Several different protocols exist and are employed for different applications but here only the main features of two commonly employed protocols will be described.

CCITT V24/RS 232C interface

The CCITT recommendation V24 defines an interface which connects a computer, or a terminal, to a modem for serial transmission over an analogue network. The USA equivalent to this recommendation is the Electronic Industries Association (EIA) specification RS 232C (or D). The use of a V24/RS 232C interface ensures that two equipments purchased from different manufacturers can be connected together and will then be able to transfer data.

The CCITT V24 and RS 232C interfaces are nearly, but not quite, identical and provide a set of interchange circuits to allow the transfer of serial data between a computer/terminal and a modem. The specified voltage levels are between $+3$ and $+15$ V for logic 0 or ON for a control circuit, and between -3 and -15 V for logic 1 or OFF for a control circuit. Very often this voltage range is limited to ± 6 V.

The V24 recommendations specify 55 interchange circuits in all but no practical interface would ever use all of them. RS 232C specifies 25 circuits although, once again, usually fewer than this number are employed. The more important circuits are listed in Table 7.1 and shown in Fig. 7.22. The functions of these selected circuits are as follows:

(*a*) Circuit 102 provides a reference against which all the other circuit voltages can be measured.

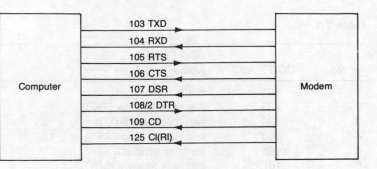

Fig. 7.22 CCITT V24/RS 232C circuits

(b) Data is sent from the terminal to the modem over circuit 103 (TXD).

(c) Data is sent from the modem to the terminal over circuit 104 (RXD).

(d) The terminal takes circuit 105 (RTS) positive to inform the modem that the terminal has data to send.

(e) The modem informs the terminal that it may now transmit its data by taking circuit 106 (CTS) positive.

(f) The modem takes circuit 109 (CD) positive to inform the terminal that it is about to receive incoming data.

(g) The modem takes circuit 107 (DSR) positive to inform the terminal that the modem is operative.

(h) Circuit 108/1 is taken positive by the terminal to instruct the modem to connect its signal conversion circuitry to the telephone line. This circuit is used when the modem operates over a leased point-to-point line.

(i) Circuit 108/2 (DTR) is taken positive by the terminal to inform the modem that the terminal is ready to transmit data. This circuit is used when the modem operates over a pstn line.

(j) Circuit 125 (CI) is only used in conjunction with a pstn line and it is taken positive when the modem has received an incoming telephone call.

The sequence of events that occur when a computer/terminal is to transfer data via a modem and a telephone line to a distant point is:

(a) The modem is switched on and connected to the telephone line; circuit DSR is turned ON.

(b) The terminal has data to transmit; circuit RTS is turned ON. The modem then transmits a carrier over the telephone line.

(c) The distant modem synchronizes itself to the received carrier and then it turns circuit CD ON.

(d) When the distant terminal is ready to receive the data it turns circuit DTR ON.

(e) The sending modem turns circuit CTS ON.

(f) The sending terminal transmits its data via the TXD circuit to the modem. At the other end of the line the data is received via the RXD circuit.

(g) When the sending terminal has no more data to send it turns its circuit RTS OFF.

(h) The sending modem removes the carrier from the line and turns its circuit CTS OFF.

(i) The distant modem loses the incoming carrier and then turns circuit CD OFF.

The RS 232C specification was revised in 1987 and the new version is known as EIA 232D; the changes are relatively minor and both versions of the interface are in common use.

HDLC synchronous protocol

The high-level data link control (HDLC) protocol is one that uses two independent channels and synchronous transmission. Messages are not sent as a number of separate characters but as a pure binary pulse train. While a binary message is being sent in one direction of transmission over one channel acknowledgements are being sent in the reverse direction over the other channel. The sending station transmits its data continuously and it only stops if an error notification is received from the distant receiver. The basic idea of the HDLC protocol is illustrated by Fig. 7.23. Three blocks of data, B_0, B_1 and B_2, are transmitted from left to right while at the same time acknowledgements ACK_0, ACK_1 and ACK_0 are sent in the other direction. The acknowledgements are alternately ACK_0 and ACK_1, regardless of how many many blocks of data are sent.

Figure 7.24 shows the format of a HDLC frame; the start flag, address field and control field together form the *header*. Each frame contains either message data or supervisory data; the latter are used to acknowledge the error-free receipt of frames, ready and busy conditions, and to report frame sequence errors. Both the start flag and the stop flag consist of the bit sequence 01111110. The address

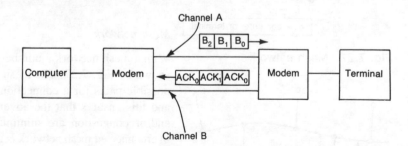

Fig. 7.23 HDLC protocol

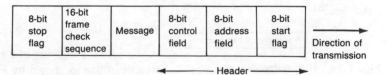

Fig. 7.24 HDLC frame format

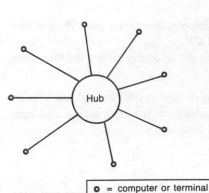

Fig. 7.25 Star network

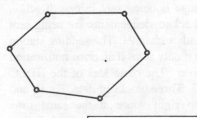

Fig. 7.26 Ring network

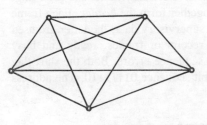

Fig. 7.27 Mesh network

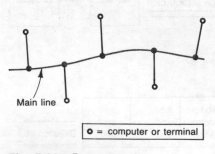

Fig. 7.28 Bus network

field holds the address of the destination terminal; it is not really necessary in a point-to-point circuit but it is always included. The control field has supervisory functions beyond the scope of this book. Lastly, the frame check sequence is used for the detection of errors.

Data networks

A private data network will contain a number of computers and terminals that need to be interconnected. A network may contain one, or more, of several different network configurations, or *topologies*.

Star network

Figure 7.25 shows the topology of a star network in which a number of computers/terminals are connected to a central *hub* by separate circuits. All communications between two terminals must go through the hub. This means that the correct operation of the network is entirely dependent upon the hub and if it should become faulty the entire network will go down. The most common application of the star network is the connection of terminals to a host computer.

Ring network

The layout of a ring network is shown by Fig. 7.26; it can be seen that it consists of a number of nodes each of which is connected to two other nodes. When data is to be sent from one node to another the message is addressed before it is transmitted into the ring. The message then circulates around the ring until the destination terminal recognizes its own address and accepts the message. A single break in the ring will not put it out of action since messages could still be transmitted in the opposite direction. The main application for the ring network is with local area networks (LANs).

Mesh network

With a mesh network a number of nodes are fully interconnected as shown by Fig. 7.27. The mesh network provides a large number of possible paths for a connection between any two desired terminals and this ensures that the adverse effects of any link/node failures and/or congestion are minimized. The disadvantage of the fully interconnected mesh network is its cost and because of this many mesh networks are only partially interconnected.

Bus network

A bus network consists of a number of terminals that are connected to a main line as shown by Fig. 7.28. The bus network is used for

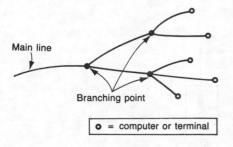

Main line

Branching point

○ = computer or terminal

Fig. 7.29 Tree network

LANs, and for other networks over fairly short distances. The main advantage of the bus network is that it is easy to add, or remove, terminals to or from the network with little, if any, disruption to its operation.

Tree network

A tree, or cluster, network is one in which a main line is split into two, or more, branches at a branching point. Each branch may, in turn, be further split into more branches up to a maximum of 12 spurs. A typical tree network is shown in Fig. 7.29.

Wide area networks

A wide area network (WAN) is a data network which covers an area greater than a few kilometres up to, possibly, the whole world. Connections between stations, computers and/or terminals, may be made over analogue or digital telephone circuits obtained from British Telecom or Mercury that may, in turn, be routed via line or radio systems. Telephone circuits are expensive and consequently various multiplexing techniques are used to enable as much data as possible to be transmitted over each line at as high a bit rate as possible.

The various transmission media employed in WANs include: dial-up connections via the pstn, leased analogue point-to-point circuits, Kilostream, Megastream, and *packet switching*. The first two named media require the use of a modem at each end of each circuit, the remainder are digital systems and so do not use a modem. When a modem is employed data can be transmitted at one of the following bit rates; 300, 600, 1200, 2400, 4800, 7200, 9600, 12 000, or 14 400 bit/s using fsk, dpsk or qam. Kilostream and Megastream are digital services provided by British Telecom. Kilostream offers bit rates of 2.4, 4.8, 9.6, 48, and 64 kbit/s; Megastream operates at 2.048, 8, 34, or 140 Mbit/s. The user of a higher-bit-rate circuit will generally employ time-division multiplexing techniques to obtain a number of lower-speed circuits. An example of a WAN is shown by Fig. 7.30; the blocks marked as MUX are multiplexers which are equipments that allow several lower-speed data circuits to be combined and transmitted as one over a higher-speed bearer circuit. The blocks marked as NTU are network terminating units and one of these is required at each end of a Kilostream circuit.

Local area networks

A local area network (LAN) is a data network that operates within a single building or between several sites separated by no more than a few kilometres. A LAN is used to interconnect computers to one

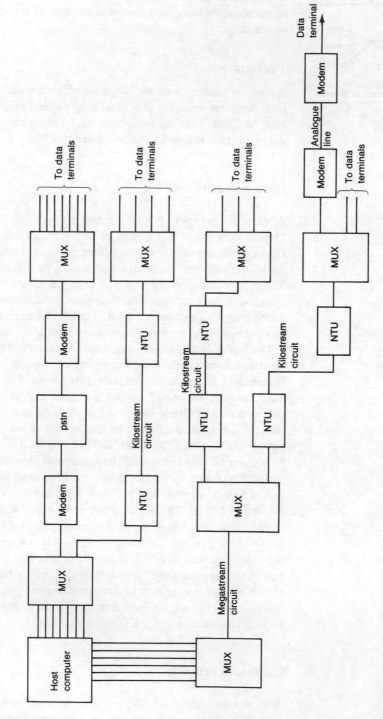

Fig. 7.30 A typical WAN

another and/or to a number of peripherals such as databases and printers. The building or site is installed with either coaxial or fibre optic cable that has a wide bandwidth; since the bandwidth limitations of the public analogue telephone network no longer apply a LAN may operate at bit rates as high as 100 Mbit/s. A LAN offers the following facilities:

(a) *Distributed processing of data* in which a number of small computers are able to access one another and/or a host computer.

(b) *Resource sharing* in which a number of computers are able to use commonly provided peripherals.

(c) *Information sharing* in which all the programs and data stored anywhere in the network are available to every user.

(d) *Network access* in which users share access to a WAN.

There arc three types of LAN in use and each of them may employ any one of the bus, ring or star topologies. The three types of LAN are known as (a) Token-passing, (b) Cambridge ring, and (c) Ethernet. Many LANs are given access to other LANs and/or a WAN and such interconnections are known as *inter-networking*.

8 Measuring instruments and measurements

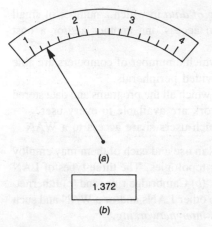

(a)

1.372

(b)

Fig. 8.1 Indication of a measured quantity by (*a*) analogue and (*b*) digital meters

The type of measuring instrument that should be used for a particular measurement depends upon the nature of the quantity to be measured, e.g. current or voltage, the frequency, the accuracy required, and the cost and availability of the various instruments. Ideally, an ammeter should have zero resistance and a voltmeter should have infinite resistance so that measurements can be taken without affecting the circuit concerned. In practice, of course, these requirements cannot be satisfied and practical ammeters have a low resistance and practical voltmeters have a high resistance.

Analogue instruments are fitted with a pointer which moves across the meter scale and its final resting position indicates the value of the quantity being measured. It is easy to misread an indication unless the observer is very careful to position his eye directly above the pointer (Avometers are provided with a glass mirror beneath the scale to make this easier). But in any case, if the pointer should be somewhere in between two scale markings, as in Fig. 8.1(*a*), some doubt must always exist about the value indicated. A linear scale, i.e., one in which equal increments indicate equal values, is easier to read than a non-linear scale since these are usually cramped at their lower-valued end. Analogue instruments include the moving-coil meter, the moving-iron meter, and the thermodynamic wattmeter. A digital instrument gives a direct visual read-out of the measured quantity, as shown by Fig. 8.1(*b*), and it is easy and quick to read.

The cathode ray oscilloscope (cro) is primarily designed for the display of signal waveforms but it can also be used for the measurement of frequency and voltage.

Some of the precautions that ought to be taken when using a measuring instrument are:

(*a*) Ensure that all the connecting leads are as short as possible and have a much smaller resistance than the meter itself. All the connections should be good and tight.

(*b*) Ensure that the instrument is in its correct physical position for indicating the measured values; this is generally either horizontal or vertical.

(*c*) Ensure that the instrument is switched for the quantity to be measured, e.g., current or voltage. Start with the highest range and then switch down step by step to the correct range; this will avoid possible damage to the instrument caused by overload.

(d) For the best accuracy using an analogue meter select a scale that positions the pointer somewhere in the upper half of the scale.

(e) Ensure that the meter affects the circuit under test as little as possible.

The moving-coil meter

Essentially, a moving-coil meter consists of a coil of wire that is placed within a radial magnetic field and that is able to rotate when it is subjected to a torque. This torque is produced by the interaction between the radial magnetic field and the field set up by a current flowing in the coil. The deflection of a pointer mounted upon the coil indicates the value of the current.

The basic construction of a moving-coil meter is shown in Figs 8.2(a), (b), and (c). A rectangular-shaped coil of fine copper wire, insulated by varnish, is wound on an aluminium former and is then mounted on a spindle so that it is free to rotate around a soft-iron cylindrical block. The pointer is fitted to the coil in such a way that as the coil rotates the pointer moves across the meter scale, see Fig. 8.2(a). The spindle is mounted at each end on jewelled bearings in order to minimize friction. Two mild steel pole pieces are fitted around the coil/cylinder assembly and their other ends are butted to a permanent magnet. The pole pieces are so shaped that a uniform magnetic field is produced in the space between the pole pieces and the cylindrical block. The rotating coil moves through this radial magnetic field in the gaps left between the pole pieces and the block,

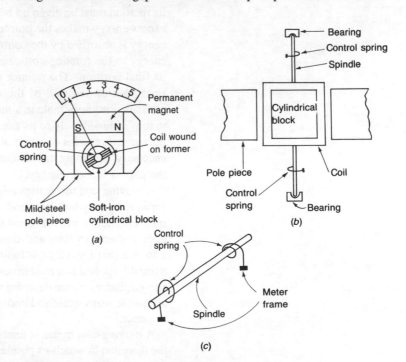

Fig. 8.2 Construction of a moving-coil meter

Fig. 8.2(*b*). The block is provided to increase the strength of the radial magnetic field. The current that is to be measured is passed into the coil via two helical springs, one at each end of the spindle as shown by Fig. 8.2(*c*). These two springs also provide a controlling torque that is directly proportional to the deflection of the pointer. Usually the control springs are made from some non-magnetic material such as phosphor bronze.

When a current is passed through the coil the magnetic field it sets up interacts with the permanent radial magnetic field to provide a torque that is directly proportional to the magnitude of the current. The coil is therefore subjected to two opposing torques; a deflecting torque due to the current being measured and a controlling torque due to the two control springs. When the deflecting and the controlling torques are equal to one another the pointer comes to rest at a point on the meter scale which, if the meter has been correctly calibrated, indicates the *mean* value of the current in the coil. Usually, an adjusting screw is provided on the face of the meter that allows the tension of one of the two control springs to be adjusted until the meter indicates zero when there is no current flowing through its coil.

Since the permanent magnetic field is radial at all points a uniform torque is applied to the coil and the ratio (angle of deflection)/(current in coil), which is known as the *sensitivity* of the meter, is a constant. The sensitivity is constant over most of each range giving a linear scale. The maximum current that can be indicated is the one that gives the *full-scale deflection* (fsd).

The moving coil has inertia and so the kinetic energy stored during its rotation must be given up before the pointer can come to rest. The excess energy makes the pointer overshoot its final position until the energy is absorbed by the control springs; the springs then return the energy to the rotating coil causing the pointer to swing back below its final position. The pointer will oscillate back and forth about its final position until all of the energy has been dissipated. Such an oscillation is undesirable in a meter because the user wants the pointer to move immediately to its final value and then stay there (assuming the current remains constant of course!). Some *damping* is therefore necessary. Damping means some method of absorbing and dissipating the excess kinetic energy.

A moving-coil meter uses *eddy-current damping*. As the aluminium former, upon which the coil is wound, moves through the radial magnetic field e.m.f.s are induced into it. The induced e.m.f.s cause eddy currents to flow and these, according to Lenz's law, produce a torque that opposes the movement of the former. The amount of damping applied to a meter must be just sufficient to make the pointer non-oscillatory. Over-damping will make the pointer too slow to move across the meter scale and under-damping will allow some oscillations to occur.

A moving-coil meter is unable to measure an a.c. current because the direction in which its pointer moves is determined by the direction in which the current flows through its coil. If an a.c. current is passed through the meter the torque applied to the coil will be reversed every half-cycle and so the average torque will be zero. This means that at low frequencies, up to about 10 Hz, the pointer will be seen to vibrate but at higher frequencies the pointer will remain on zero reading.

The principal causes of error in a moving-coil meter are: (*a*) friction between moving parts, (*b*) temperature effects, and (*c*) interfering magnetic fields. Errors can also be caused by the meter resistance affecting a circuit and this is dealt with later.

The moving-iron meter

There are two kinds of moving-iron meter; these are (*a*) the attraction type and (*b*) the repulsion type. Both types are able to measure both a.c. and d.c. currents and both have a non-linear scale, but since the repulsion type is the more commonly employed only this type will be described in this chapter.

The basic construction of a moving-iron meter is shown by Fig. 8.3. Two pieces of iron are positioned inside a coil; one of the pieces is fixed in its position while the other piece is mounted on a spindle and is free to move. When a current is passed through the coil it sets up a magnetic field around the coil. This magnetic field magnetizes both pieces of iron with the same polarization and, since like poles repel, the moving iron moves away from the larger end of the fixed iron towards its smaller end where the repulsive force is smaller. The movement is controlled by the opposing force exerted by the control springs and continues until the deflecting and controlling torques become equal to one another. The pointer is fixed to the moving iron and it is deflected across the meter scale as the moving iron moves.

Damping is achieved by the movement of a piston inside a closed cylinder. The resistance to piston movement offered by the air trapped inside the cylinder is sufficient to prevent the pointer from oscillating about its final position.

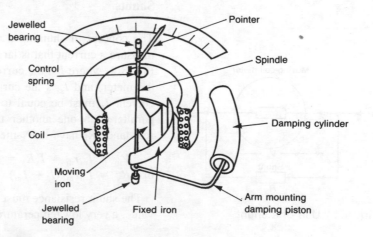

Fig. 8.3 Construction of a moving-iron meter

The current range of a moving-iron meter can be increased by tapping the coil at various points which allows the current to flow through a reduced number of turns. If, for example, the use of a tap meant that only one-half of the coil's turns are used then the fsd of the meter will be increased by four times compared with using all the turns. The relative merits of moving-coil and moving-iron meters are as follows:

(a) The moving-coil meter has a linear scale but the moving-iron meter has not.
(b) The moving-coil meter suffers less interference from external magnetic fields,
(c) The moving-coil meter has the greater sensitivity.
(d) The moving-coil meter dissipates less power.
(e) The moving-iron meter is the more robust.
(f) The moving-iron meter can measure both a.c. and d.c. currents but the moving-coil meter can only measure d.c. currents.
(g) The moving-iron meter is cheaper.

Shunts and multipliers

A moving-coil meter has a fairly low resistance, normally somewhere in the range 3 ohms to about 100 ohms or so. The current that flows through the meter to move the pointer to the top end of the scale is known as the full-scale deflection (fsd) and it is typically 1 to 20 mA. If a larger current than that giving fsd is to be measured it is necessary to bypass a known fraction of the current from the meter and through a parallel-connected resistor known as a *shunt*. The maximum voltage that can be allowed across the meter is equal to the product of the fsd current and the meter resistance. If a larger voltage than this is to be measured the excess voltage must be dropped across a series resistor known as a *multiplier*.

Shunts

The concept of shunting a moving-coil meter so that it is able to measure a current that is larger than the fsd current is illustrated by Fig. 8.4, where I is the current to be measured, I_m is the current in the meter, and I_s is the current that flows in the shunt. The shunt current I_s must be equal to $I - I_m$. Since they are connected in parallel with one another the meter resistance r_m and the shunt resistance R_s have the same voltage V_m across them. Therefore,

$$V_m = I_m r_m = I_s R_s = (I - I_m)R_s,$$
$$\text{or} \quad R_s = I_m r_m/(I - I_m). \tag{8.1}$$

The shunt resistance must have precisely the calculated resistance value, a very low temperature coefficient of resistance, be stable with

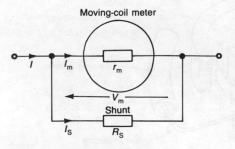

Moving-coil meter

I I_m r_m

V_m

Shunt

I_s R_s

Fig. 8.4 Use of a shunt

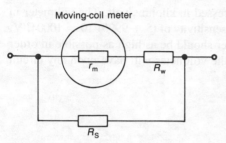

Fig. 8.5 Overcoming error due to temperature changes

time, be made from a non-corrosive material such as manganin, and have a relatively large surface area so that any heat produced in it is easily dissipated. The resistance of the meter may vary with change in temperature and should this occur the accuracy of the shunted meter will be adversely affected. The potential error can be minimized by connecting a resistor in series with the meter as shown by Fig. 8.5; this resistance usually has a value of about three times the meter resistance.

Example 8.1

A moving-coil meter has a resistance of $4\,\Omega$ and an fsd current of 15 mA. Calculate the value of the shunt resistance needed to allow the meter to measure currents up to (a) 5 A, and (b) 50 A.

Solution

(a) From equation (8.1),
$$R_s = (15 \times 10^{-3} \times 4)/(5 - 15 \times 10^{-3}) = 12.04\,\text{m}\Omega. \quad (Ans.)$$
(b) $R_s = (15 \times 10^{-3} \times 4)/(50 - 15 \times 10^{-3}) = 1.2\,\text{m}\Omega. \quad (Ans.)$

Multipliers

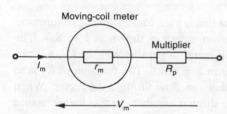

Fig. 8.6 Use of a multiplier

A multiplier resistance is required to allow a meter to measure a voltage that is larger than the maximum permitted voltage drop across the meter. The multiplier is connected in series with the meter as shown by Fig. 8.6. From the figure, $V_m = I_m(r_m + R_p)$, or

$$R_p = (V_m - I_m r_m)/I_m. \quad (8.2)$$

The higher the voltage to be measured the higher must be the resistance of the multiplier. A multi-meter will be provided with switches to allow the meter to (a) measure either current or resistance, and (b) insert various shunts or multipliers to give different ranges of current or voltage.

Example 8.2

A moving-coil meter has a resistance of $5\,\Omega$ and a fsd current of 1 mA. The meter is to be used to measure currents of up to 100 mA and voltages of up to 10 V. Calculate the required values of (a) the shunt resistance, and (b) the multiplier resistance.

Solution

The maximum voltage across the meter $= 1 \times 10^{-3} \times 5 = 5\,\text{mV}$.

(a) Shunt resistance $= (5 \times 10^{-3})/(99 \times 10^{-3}) = 50.51\,\text{m}\Omega. \quad (Ans.)$
(b) Multiplier resistance $= (10 - 5 \times 10^{-3})/(1 \times 10^{-3})$
$$= 9995\,\Omega. \quad (Ans.)$$

At fsd the ratio (circuit resistance)/voltage is known as the *sensitivity* of a voltmeter and it is expressed in kilohms/volt. The voltmeter in Example 8.2 therefore has a sensitivity of $(5 + 9995)/10 = 1000\,\Omega/V$. The sensitivity of a voltmeter should be as high as possible in order to minimize the effect that the voltmeter will have upon any circuit to which it is connected.

Example 8.3

A moving-coil voltmeter has a sensitivity of 20 kΩ/V and it is to be used to measure voltages in the range 0–60 V. If the meter has a resistance of 20 Ω calculate the required multiplier resistance.

Solution
The fsd current $= 1/(20 \times 10^3) = 50\,\mu A$, and the fsd voltage is to be 60 V. The required circuit resistance $= 60/(50 \times 10^{-6}) = 1.2\,M\Omega$. Therefore, the multiplier resistance $= 1.2\,M\Omega - 20\,\Omega = 1\,199\,980\,\Omega$.

(Ans.)

Shunts are rarely used in conjunction with moving-iron meters although multipliers are employed. When the current range of a moving-iron meter is to be increased a *current transformer* is normally used.

The ohm meter

An ohm meter is an instrument that is used for the direct measurement of resistance and its basic arrangement is shown in Fig. 8.7. The instrument uses a moving-coil meter, a parallel resistor R_1, a series resistor R_2 and a battery of e.m.f. E volts. The function of R_2 is to limit the maximum current that can flow through the meter. When the terminals of the meter are shorted together, so that the resistance between them is zero, the current I_{sc} that flows is

$$I_{sc} = E/[R_2 + r_m R_1/(r_m + R_1)].$$

The resistance R_1 can then be adjusted until the meter indicates its fsd current; the pointer will then be at the right-hand side of the scale and it is calibrated as zero ohms. This adjustment should always be

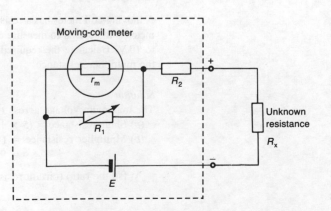

Fig. 8.7 The ohm meter

carried out before a resistance is measured and it is necessary because the battery voltage will vary with time. The maximum resistance reading occurs when the terminals of the ohm meter are open-circuited and zero current flows in the meter. The pointer is then at the extreme left-hand side of the scale and this point is marked as infinity ohms.

To carry out a resistance measurement the meter zero is first set and then the resistance to be measured is connected across the meter terminals. The resistance can then be read directly from the meter scale. A practical ohm meter will be used to measure resistances over a wide range of values and the scales can be changed by switching into circuit different values of resistor R_2 and, perhaps, of the battery voltage E.

Example 8.4

An unknown resistor R_x is being measured using the ohm meter shown in Fig. 8.7. The component values of the ohm meter are: $R_1 = 1450\,\Omega$, $r_m\|R_1 = 50\,\Omega$, and $E = 1.5$ V. The fsd current is 1 mA. Calculate the value of R_x when the meter deflection is (a) 0.25 fsd, and (b) 0.8 fsd.

Solution
(a) 0.25 fsd = 0.25 mA.
$1.5/(0.25 \times 10^{-3}) = 50 + 1450 + R_x$,
or $R_x = 4500\,\Omega$. (*Ans.*)
(b) 0.8 fsd = 0.8 mA.
$1.5/(0.8 \times 10^{-3}) = 1500 + R_x$,
or $R_x = 375\,\Omega$. (*Ans.*)

When an ohm meter is used it should be noted that the terminal marked + actually has a negative potential with respect to the terminal marked −. This makes no difference when a resistor is measured but it does when the resistance of a diode or the resistance of the base/emitter junction of a bipolar transistor is measured. The resistance between two points in a circuit should not be measured while the circuit has its power supplies switched on since any voltage present in that part of the circuit will give erroneous results and could, possibly, damage the meter.

Rectifier instruments

A moving-coil meter can only be used to measure an a.c. current if that current is first rectified. The basic arrangement of a rectifier instrument is shown by Fig. 8.8. The a.c. current to be measured is applied to the bridge rectifier and the resulting d.c. current flows though the moving-coil meter. If the a.c. current is of sinusoidal waveform the rectified current will have the waveform given in Fig. 8.9. The average value of a half-sinewave is $0.637\,I_m$, where I_m is the peak value (p. 79). The deflection of the pointer is directly proportional to the mean value of the current. Ammeters and voltmeters are, however, usually calibrated to indicate the r.m.s. value

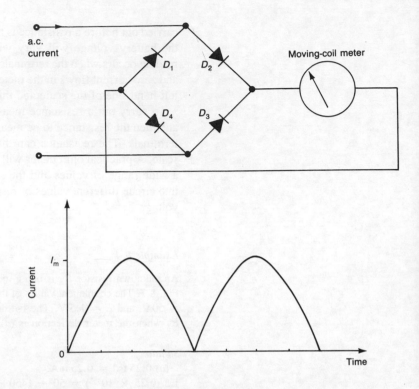

Fig. 8.8 Rectifier instrument

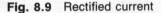

Fig. 8.9 Rectified current

of a sinusoidal waveform. This means that the meter scale is marked with values that are 1.11 times the mean current actually indicated. The figure 1.11 is used because, it is, of course, the form factor (r.m.s. value)/(mean value) of a sinusoidal waveform.

Unfortunately, this calibration practice means that a rectifier instrument will indicate incorrectly whenever it is used to measure a current, or voltage, that has a non-sinusoidal waveform. Square and rectangular waveforms will give high readings and pulse-like waveforms will give low readings.

Many rectifier instruments are able to work at frequencies up to about 100 kHz but they are not suitable for d.c. measurements.

Example 8.5

A triangular waveform is measured using a rectifier instrument when the meter indication is 6 V. Calculate (a) the true reading, and (b) the percentage error in the reading.

Solution

For a triangular wave of peak value V_m the mean value is $V_m/2$ and the r.m.s. value is $V_m/\sqrt{3}$.

The meter indication = $1.11 \times V_m/2 = 6$ V and therefore $V_m = 12/1.11$ = 10.811 V.

(a) True reading = $10.811/\sqrt{3} = 6.242$ V.   (*Ans.*)
(b) Percentage error = $[(6.242 - 6)/6.242] \times 100$
                    = $+3.87\%$.   (*Ans.*)

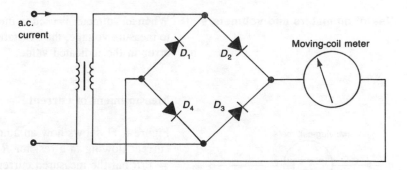

Fig. 8.10 Increasing the current range of a rectifier instrument

A shunt is not used to increase the range of a rectifier instrument because of the non-linear current/voltage characteristics of the diodes. Instead, the bridge rectifier is supplied from the secondary winding of an input transformer as shown by Fig. 8.10. Different current ranges are obtained by tapping the *primary* winding at various points to obtain different current transformation ratios. The voltage range of a rectifier instrument can be increased by the use of multipliers.

Multi-meters

Clearly, it would prove convenient for the user to be able to use just the one instrument for the measurement of both a.c. and d.c. currents and voltages and also for resistance measurements, and this is what a multi-meter is able to do. The best-known multi-meter is the AVOmeter and the outline specification for the AVO model 6 is given in Table 8.1.

Table 8.1

Ranges

d.c. voltage:	100 mV, 3 V, 10 V, 30 V, 100 V, 600 V, 1000 V
a.c. voltage:	3 V, 10 V, 30 V, 300 V, 600 V, 1000 V
d.c. current:	50 μA, 300 μA, 1 mA, 10 mA, 100 mA, 1 A, 10 A
a.c. current:	10 mA, 100 mA, 1 A, 10 A
resistance:	0–2 kΩ, 0–200 kΩ, 0–20 MΩ

Accuracy at 20 °C

d.c. ranges:	±1% of fsd
a.c. ranges:	±2% of fsd
resistance ranges	+3% of centre-scale reading

Sensitivity

d.c. voltage ranges:	20 kΩ/V
a.c. voltage 3 V range:	100 Ω/V
10 V range:	1000 Ω/V
all other ranges:	2000 Ω/V

Use of ammeters and voltmeters

When an ammeter is used to measure current, or a voltmeter is used to measure voltage, the resistance of the meter itself will produce an error in the indicated value.

Measurement of current

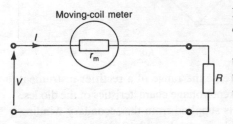

Moving-coil meter

Fig. 8.11 Measurement of current

Figure 8.11 shows how an ammeter would be used to measure the current flowing in a resistor R. The true value of the current is $I_t = V/R$ but the measured current is $I_m = V/(R + r_m)$, where r_m is the resistance of the ammeter. The meter resistance is in series with the resistor R and so the measured current will be smaller than the true value that flowed before the ammeter was inserted into the circuit.

Example 8.6

An ammeter has a resistance of 20 Ω and is used to measure the current that flows in a 1000 Ω resistor when 12 V are applied across it. Calculate the percentage error in the measurement.

Solution

Before the meter was inserted into the circuit the current flowing was equal to 12/1000 = 12 mA. The measured current is 12/1020 = 11.765 mA. Therefore, the percentage error is
$$[(11.765 - 12)/12] \times 100\% = -1.96\%. \quad (Ans.)$$

Measurement of voltage

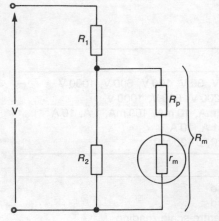

Fig. 8.12 Measurement of voltage

Figure 8.12 shows a circuit consisting of two resistors R_1 and R_2 connected in series across a voltage supply of V volts. The voltage dropped across resistor R_2 is to be measured using a voltmeter whose internal resistance is R_m ohms, $R_m = r_m$ + multiplier resistance R_p. The true voltage across R_2 is $V_{2t} = VR_2/(R_1 + R_2)$. When the voltmeter is connected across R_2 to measure the voltage across it the voltmeter's resistance R_m is placed in parallel with R_2 to give an effective resistance of $R_p = R_2R_m/(R_2 + R_m)$. The indicated voltage is then $V_{2m} = VR_p/(R_1 + R_p)$ and this will be lower than the true value of the voltage.

Example 8.7

Two 12 kΩ resistors are connected in series across a 6 V supply. The voltage across one of the resistors is measured using a voltmeter that has a resistance of 20 kΩ. Calculate the percentage error in the indicated voltage.

Solution

The true voltage = 3 V.
The effective resistance R_p of a 12 kΩ resistor and the voltmeter resistance

in parallel is $R_p = (12 \times 20)/(12 + 20) = 7.5$ kΩ. The indicated voltage is $(6 \times 7.5)/(12 + 7.5) = 2.308$ V. The percentage error in the measurement is $[(2.308 - 3)/3] \times 100 = -23.1\%$.   (*Ans.*)

Measurement of resistance

The resistance of a resistor can be measured using an ammeter and a voltmeter since resistance = voltage/current. There are two ways in which the two meters may be connected and these are shown by Figs 8.13(*a*) and (*b*). In (*a*) the ammeter indicates the sum of the currents that flow in the resistor and in the voltmeter. The voltmeter correctly indicates the voltage across the resistor. The true value of the resistance is $R = V/I$ but the measured value is $R = V/(I_R + I_m)$ and this will be lower than the true resistance. In the alternative connection, Fig. 8.13(*b*), the ammeter correctly indicates the current in the resistor, but now the voltmeter indicates the sum of the voltages, V_R and V_m, across the resistor R and the ammeter respectively. Now the measured resistance is $R = (V_R + V_m)/I$ and this will be higher than the true value of the resistor.

The choice between the two connections depends upon which of them will give the least error in the measured resistance. This, in turn, depends upon the relative values of the unknown resistance and the resistances of the two meters. For the circuit of Fig. 8.13(*a*) the error is least when the voltmeter resistance is very much larger than the unknown resistance. Conversely, for the other circuit, (*b*), the error is least when the ammeter resistance is very much smaller than the unknown resistance. This means that the circuit shown in Fig. 8.13(*a*) should be used to measure low values of resistance and the other circuit should be used when a high value of resistance is to be measured.

Example 8.8

A 2200 Ω resistance is measured using the ammeter/voltmeter method. The ammeter has a resistance of 5 Ω and the voltmeter has a resistance of 20 kΩ. Calculate the percentage error in the measurement when the circuit used is (*a*) Fig. 8.13(*a*), and (*b*) Fig. 8.13(*b*).

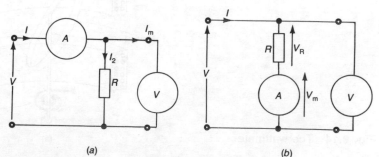

Fig. 8.13   Measurement of resistance

(*a*)   (*b*)

Solution

Assume the applied voltage is 1 V.

(a) Resistance of circuit = $5 + (2200 \times 20 \times 10^3)/(2200 + 20 \times 10^3)$ = $5 + 1982 = 1987 \,\Omega$. The current $I = 1/1987 = 0.503$ mA. The measured resistance is $1/(0.503 \times 10^{-3}) = 1987 \,\Omega$. Therefore, the percentage error = $[(1987 - 2200)/2200 = -9.68\%$. (*Ans.*)

(b) Voltage across meter = 1 V.

Current in $R = 1/2205 = 0.454$ mA. Measured resistance = $1/(0.454 \times 10^{-3}) = 2205 \,\Omega$.

Therefore, the percentage error = $[(2205 - 2200)/2200] \times 100$
$$= +0.23\%. \quad (Ans.)$$

The wattmeter

The wattmeter is an instrument that has been designed to measure power in watts. Essentially, a wattmeter consists of two fixed coils inside which there is one moving coil. Two views of a wattmeter are shown in Figs 8.14(a) and (b). The moving coil is mounted upon a spindle that is held at each end by bearings. The necessary controlling torque is, as with the moving-coil meter, provided by two helical springs. These springs are also often used to take the current into and out of the moving coil. When a current, a.c. or d.c., is passed through the two fixed coils a uniform magnetic field is set up in the space inside the coils. If the moving coil has a current *at the same frequency* (which could be 0 Hz), the magnetic field it sets up will interact with the fixed coil's field to produce a torque on the moving coil. This torque is always exerted in the same direction and it is directly proportional to the product of the currents in the fixed and the moving coils. The torque causes the moving coil to rotate, against the restraining force exerted by the control springs, and this rotation moves the pointer across the meter scale. The wattmeter is a form of electrodynamic instrument.

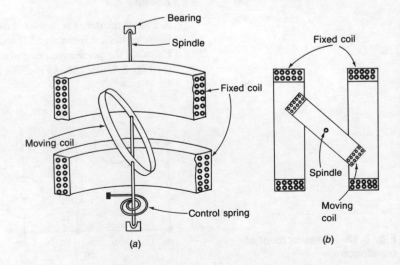

Fig. 8.14 The wattmeter

(a)

(b)

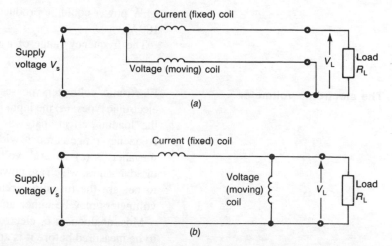

Fig. 8.15 Two ways of connecting a wattmeter

For an electrodynamic instrument to measure power the fixed and the moving coils must be connected in the manner shown by either Fig. 8.15(a) or Fig. 8.15(b). The fixed coils must be wound with relatively few turns of thick wire and the moving coil wound with many turns of fine wire. In both circuits the fixed, or current, coils are connected in series with one another and with the load, and the moving, or voltage, coil is connected in parallel with the load. The current flowing in the current coils will be proportional to the load current, and the current in the voltage coil will be proportional to the load voltage. The torque exerted upon the moving coil is thus proportional to the mean product of the load current and the load voltage, i.e., to the load power. The instrument therefore acts as a wattmeter. When an a.c. power is measured the inductive reactance of the voltage coil may be large enough to give a noticeable phase difference between the current in the voltage coil and the load voltage. This will lead to an error in the indicated power; this error can be reduced by the connection of a non-reactive resistor in series with the voltage coil.

Both connections have inherent errors in the indicated power because of internal wattmeter power dissipation. If the resistances of the current and voltage coils are R_c and R_v respectively, then for circuit (a), current in current coil = I_L and current in voltage coil = V_s/R_v. The meter indication is proportional to $I_L V_s$ and so there is an error equal to $I_L V_s - I_L V_L = I_L^2 R_c$. Thus the error is caused by the power that is dissipated in the current coil. For connection (b), current in current coil = $I_L + V_L/R_v$ and so the meter indication = $V_L(I_L + V_L/R_v) = V_L I_L + V_L^2/R_v$, which gives an error of V_L^2/R_v. Thus, now the error is due to the power that is dissipated in the voltage coil.

When using the wattmeter the connection that should be chosen is the one that introduces the smallest measurement error and this depends upon the values of the load current and the load voltage, e.g.,

1 kW power could be produced by 1 A and 1000 V, or by 10 A and 100 V.

The frequency range of a wattmeter is limited to about 100 Hz.

The electronic voltmeter

Electronic voltmeters possess a number of advantages over non-electronic types: (*a*) the input impedance can be very high, eliminating the loading effect that was illustrated by Example 8.7, (*b*) the frequency range is much wider and may well go as high as several megahertz, (*c*) several voltage ranges are provided. The main disadvantages, which are nowadays nowhere as important as they used to be, are the (usually) greater cost and physical size. Electronic voltmeters may be either analogue or digital types.

Most analogue a.c. electronic voltmeters rectify the a.c. voltage to be measured before it is applied to a variable-gain d.c. amplifier. Usually, a peak detector is employed and Fig. 8.16 shows the basic block diagram of such an electronic voltmeter. The a.c. voltage to be measured is applied to the peak detector and this produces a d.c. output voltage that is directly proportional to the peak value of the a.c. voltage. The d.c. voltage is then applied to a variable attenuator which introduces a set amount of loss depending upon the position of the range switch. The attenuated voltage is amplified by the d.c. amplifier to produce a d.c. current that is passed through the moving-coil meter. The scale of the meter is calibrated to indicate the r.m.s. value of a sinusoidal input voltage; this means that all scale markings are 0.707 times the indicated peak value. Once again this means that a measurement error occurs whenever a non-sinusoidal voltage is measured. An a.c./d.c. voltmeter will have a switched input so that d.c. voltages can be applied directly to the attenuator stage.

A digital voltmeter is able to measure an input voltage and give a visual read-out of its value on an LED display. The basic block diagram of a digital voltmeter is shown by Fig. 8.17. The ramp generator provides a ramp, or sawtooth, waveform and its output is applied to the inverting input of an op-amp. In the absence of an input voltage the output of the ramp generator will be more positive than the potential at the non-inverting input of the op-amp. The output of

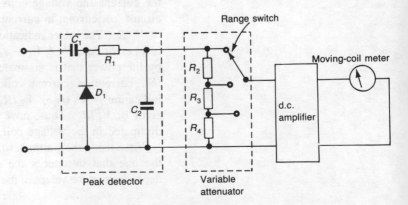

Fig. 8.16 Electronic voltmeter

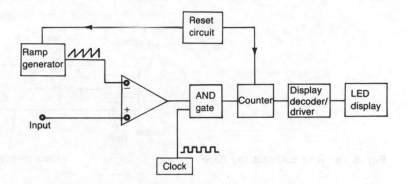

Fig. 8.17 Digital voltmeter

the op-amp will then be at a negative voltage and this will disable the AND gate. No clock pulses are then able to pass through the gate and reach the counter. Both the ramp generator and the counter are reset to zero at regular intervals of time by reset pulses provided by a clock in the reset circuit.

When an input signal is applied to the voltmeter it will be larger than the reset ramp voltage. Since it is applied to the non-inverting input of the op-amp the output of the op-amp will be at a positive voltage and the AND gate is enabled. Clock pulses are then able to pass through the gate to arrive at the counter input. The counter starts counting the clock pulses. Once the ramp voltage has increased to the point at which it has become slightly more positive than the input voltage the op-amp switches state so that its output voltage goes negative. This negative voltage disables the AND gate and no more clock pulses can reach the counter. The count ceases and when the counter is next reset the count is passed to the display decoder circuit and here it is changed into the form required to activate the LED display; the display then provides a visual read-out of the input voltage.

When an a.c. voltage is to be measured the input signal is first rectified to provide a d.c. voltage input to the digital meter proper. The meter is calibrated to give the r.m.s. value of a sinusoidal input voltage.

The cathode ray oscilloscope

A cathode ray oscilloscope (cro) is an instrument that gives a visual display of signal waveforms on the screen of a cathode ray tube (crt). A cro can be used to observe waveforms, to measure voltage and time, and to determine the phase difference between two signals. A cro may have a single beam when only one waveform may be displayed at a time, or it may be a dual-beam instrument allowing two waveforms to be simultaneously displayed.

The cathode ray tube

The basic construction of a crt is shown in Fig. 8.18. The tube consists of an evacuated glass envelope inside which there are an *electron gun*,

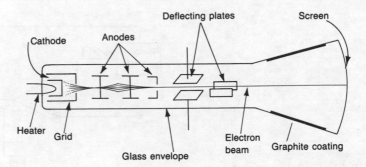

Fig. 8.18 The cathode ray tube

focusing and deflecting electrodes, and a fluorescent screen. The electron gun consists of a cathode surrounded by a cylindrical modulator, or grid, which is kept at a negative potential relative to the cathode. Electrons emitted from the cathode are attracted by the positive potential, relative to the grid, on the first anode and they pass through a hole in the end of the grid. The electric fields set up between the grid and the three anodes focus the electron beam at a point somewhere past the last anode. By adjustment of the relative potentials applied to the anodes this point is made to coincide with the screen. Usually only the potential applied to the middle anode is variable by means of the focus control. The inside of the screen is coated with a fluorescent material, such as zinc orthosilicate, and this glows visibly when it is struck by electrons. The position of the electron beam is thus indicated by a visible spot of light. The brightness of the spot is determined by the number of electrons striking the screen and this is controlled by the grid potential and it can be varied by the brightness control.

Between the final anode and the screen are located two pairs of deflecting plates, known as the X plates and the Y plates. The X plates produce a horizontal electric field to deflect the electron beam in the horizontal plane; the Y plates provide deflection in the vertical plane. The principle of electric deflection of the electron beam is shown by Figs 8.19(a), (b) and (c). In (a) and (b) the electron beam is deflected towards the positive plate. If voltages are applied to both the X and the Y plates, (c), at the same time the electron beam will be subjected to simultaneous horizontal and vertical forces and it will be deflected in the resultant direction. The amount by which the electron beam

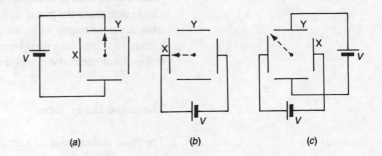

Fig. 8.19 Electric deflection of the electron beam

(a)   (b)   (c)

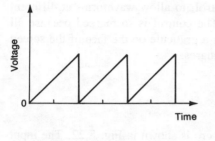

Fig. 8.20 Timebase voltage

is deflected per volt applied across a pair of deflecting plates is known as the *deflection sensitivity* of the plates. The deflection sensitivity is inversely proportional to the accelerating potential on the final anode. However, since the spot brightness depends upon the acceleration of the electron beam, and hence on the final anode voltage, the final anode voltage cannot be reduced. Many crts therefore have another anode between the deflecting plates and the screen to give *post-deflection acceleration*. This extra anode usually takes the form of a graphite coating on the inside wall of the tube which is connected to the final anode.

For an a.c. voltage to be displayed on the crt screen a sawtooth voltage, see Fig. 8.20, must be applied to the X plates. The sawtooth voltage is produced by a circuit known as the *timebase*. The timebase voltage moves the electron beam with a constant velocity in the horizontal plane and hence a visible spot of light moves across the screen from left to right. When the spot has moved completely across the screen the ramp voltage is suddenly reduced to zero; this causes the visible spot to *fly-back* to the left-hand side of the screen at a very fast rate. During the fly-back period the display is blanked off so that the spot cannot be seen. Because the afterglow of the fluorescent material is short only a small area of the screen is actually glowing at any instant, but because of the persistence of vision of the human eye a continuous horizontal line is seen.

If an a.c. voltage is applied across the Y plates it will cause the electron beam to be simultaneously deflected in the vertical plane as well. If the periodic times of the timebase and signal voltages are equal to one another, or one is a low integer multiple of the other, the visible spot will describe the correct waveform on the screen. The idea is illustrated by Fig. 8.21. The frequency of the timebase can be adjusted,

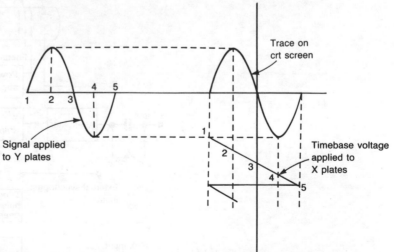

Fig. 8.21 Derivation of the trace on the crt screen

by means of the time/cm control, to allow waveforms at different frequencies to be observed. The control is so marked because all measurements are made using a graticule on the face of the screen that is engraved with 1 cm squares.

The cathode ray oscilloscope

The basic block diagram of a cro is shown in Fig. 8.22. The input circuit consists of an input attenuator and a Y amplifier. The voltage applied to the Y plates must lie within a given range of values, and the function of the attenuator and the Y amplifier is to adjust the input signal's amplitude to be within this range. The attenuator is calibrated in V/cm so that the graticule markings can represent so many volts per centimetre. Direct coupling can be used to allow slowly varying signals to be observed or a capacitor can be switched, using the a.c./d.c. switch, into the input circuit to remove any d.c. component from an applied signal. Horizontal deflection of the spot is provided by the timebase generator and the X amplifier. The timebase generator may be operated as either a free-running circuit or as a triggered circuit; in the triggered case the sawtooth voltage is not continuous but starts each ramp upon the receipt of a trigger pulse. Triggered operation is required when the waveform to be displayed does not recur at regular intervals. When it is free-running the timebase generator is synchronized, either by pulses derived from the input signal (taken from the Y amplifier) or by an external synchronization signal. For some measurements it is necessary to be able to switch

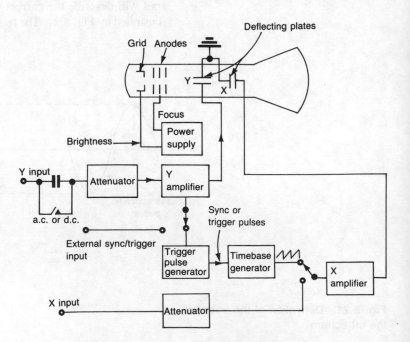

Fig. 8.22 Block diagram of a cro

off the internal timebase generator and to apply an external voltage to the X amplifier, Fig. 8.22 shows how this is done.

Two other controls, X shift and Y shift, allow the user to move the visible trace in the horizontal and vertical directions.

Most cros are of the dual-beam type and Fig. 8.23 shows a typical block diagram of such an instrument. It can be seen to have two separate input circuits, complete with attenuators and amplifiers, and a single common timebase.

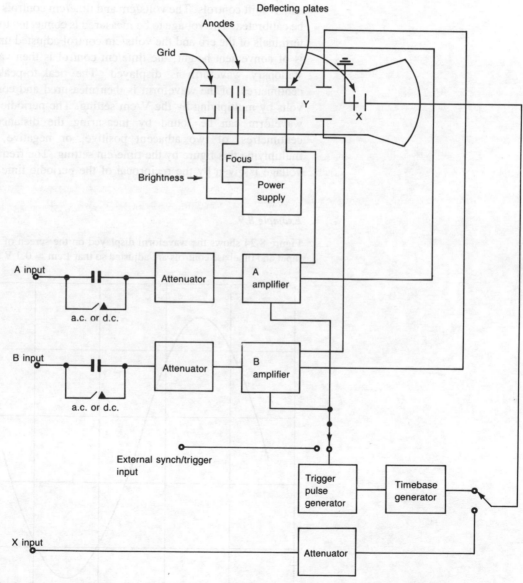

Fig. 8.23 Block diagram of dual-beam cro

Use of the cro

A cro can be used to measure the peak voltage and the frequency of a displayed waveform by measuring the number of centimetres occupied on the screen by both the peak-to-peak value and the periodic time. Before a cro is used for a measurement it should be switched on and allowed to warm up for several minutes. The trigger control should then be adjusted to give a visible horizontal line before the brilliance and focus controls are set to obtain a sharp, bright, trace. The position of the trace should then be adjusted using the X-shift and Y-shift controls. The volts/cm and time/cm controls should then be calibrated. The voltage to be measured is connected to the Y input terminals of the cro and the volts/cm control adjusted until the trace is of convenient height; the time/cm control is then varied until a stationary waveform is displayed. The peak-to-peak value, in centimetres, of the waveform is then measured and converted into volts by multiplying by the V/cm setting. The periodic time of the waveform can be found by measuring the distance apart, in centimetres, of two adjacent positive, or negative, peaks and multiplying this figure by the time/cm setting. The frequency of the voltage is given by the reciprocal of the periodic time.

Example 8.9

Figure 8.24 shows the waveform displayed on the screen of a cro. The Y input and timebase controls are adjusted so that 1 cm = 0.1 V in the vertical

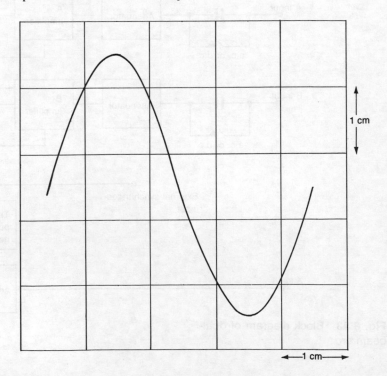

1 cm

←—1 cm—→

Fig. 8.24

direction and 1 cm = 10 μs in the horizontal direction. Calculate the peak value and the frequency of the waveform.

Solution
Peak-to-peak value = 4 cm = 0.4 V and so the peak value = 0.2 V.   (*Ans.*)
 The spacing between one positive peak and the next is 4 cm; hence the periodic time is 40 μs and the frequency is 25 kHz.   (*Ans.*)

Example 8.10

The square waveform shown in Fig. 8.25 is displayed on the screen of a cro that has its a.c./d.c. switch in the a.c. position. The timebase control is set at 10 μs/cm and the volts/cm control is set to 10 V/cm. Calculate (*a*) the peak-to-peak voltage, (*b*) the periodic time, and (*c*) the frequency of the waveform.
 When the a.c./d.c. switch is moved to its d.c. position the displayed waveform (i) remains unchanged, and (ii) moves upwards by 1 cm. For each case calculate (*d*) the mean value of the waveform, and (*e*) its positive and negative peak values.

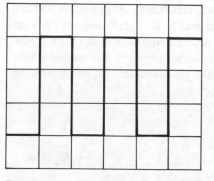

Fig. 8.25

Solution
 (*a*) Peak-to-peak value = 3 cm = 30 V.   (*Ans.*)
 (*b*) Periodic time = 2 cm = 20 μs.   (*Ans.*)
 (*c*) Frequency = $1/(20 \times 10^{-6})$ = 50 kHz.   (*Ans.*)
 (*d*) (i) Mean value = 0 V; (ii) mean value = 1 cm = 10 V.   (*Ans.*)
 (*e*) (i) Positive peak value = negative peak value = 15 V; (ii) positive peak value = 15 + 10 = 25 V; negative value = $-15 + 10 = -5$ V.
    (*Ans.*)

The Wheatstone bridge

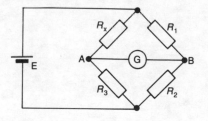

Fig. 8.26 The Wheatstone bridge

A Wheatstone bridge consists of four resistors connected together to form a bridge network as shown by Fig. 8.26. If a d.c. voltage source of e.m.f. *E* volts is connected across two opposite sides of the bridge a current will flow in a galvanometer connected between the two other sides. The magnitude and direction of the galvanometer current depend upon the degree of imbalance of the bridge. The Wheatstone bridge can be used to determine the value of an unknown resistance R_x by *balancing* the bridge. The bridge is said to be balanced when zero current flows through the galvanometer, a condition indicated by a centre-zero reading. The balance condition is reached by adjustment of the variable resistor R_1; the other two resistors are known as the ratio resistances. The values of all three resistors, R_1, R_2 and R_3, must be accurately known.
 For the bridge to be balanced the p.d. between the points A and B must be zero or else a current would flow through the galvanometer. This means that (*a*) the potential of point A must be equal to the potential of point B, (*b*) the currents flowing in resistors R_1 and R_2 must be equal, say I_1, and (*c*) the currents flowing in resistors R_x and R_3 must be equal, say I_x. Then,

$$I_1 R_1 = I_x R_x \qquad (8.3)$$
$$I_1 R_2 = I_x R_3 \qquad (8.4)$$

Dividing equation (8.3) by equation (8.4) gives

$$R_1/R_2 = R_x/R_3 \quad \text{or} \quad R_1R_3 = R_xR_2 \tag{8.5}$$

Equation (8.5) shows that the bridge is balanced when the *products of the resistances of the opposite arms are equal*. The value of the unknown resistance R_x is then given by equation (8.6), i.e.,

$$R_x = R_1R_3/R_2 \tag{8.6}$$

R_3/R_2 is the ratio by which the value of the variable resistor R_1 must be multiplied to give the value of the unknown resistance. This is why they are known as the ratio resistances. At balance no current flows through the galvanometer and so the supply voltage does not appear in the balance equation and it therefore does not matter what its value happens to be. Often an audio-frequency a.c. voltage source is used as the supply and then the galvanometer will be replaced by headphones as the bridge detector.

Example 8.11

A Wheatstone bridge is balanced when $R_1 = 15\,\Omega$, $R_2 = 200\,\Omega$ and $R_3 = 1000\,\Omega$. Calculate the value of the unknown resistance.

Solution
From equation (8.6),
$$R_x = (15 \times 1000)/200 = 75\,\Omega. \quad (Ans.)$$

Exercises

Chapter 1

1.1 For the circuit shown in Fig. E.1 calculate (*a*) the current taken from the supply, (*b*) the current in the 3.9 kΩ resistor, and (*c*) the power dissipated in the 6.2 kΩ resistor.

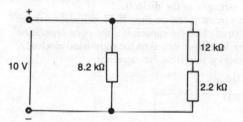

Fig. E.1

1.2 For the circuit shown in Fig. E.2 calculate (*a*) the power dissipated in the 8.2 kΩ resistor, (*b*) the voltage across the 2.2 kΩ resistor, and (*c*) the current flowing in each resistor and the supply current.

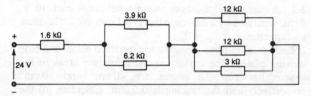

Fig. E.2

1.3 Calculate (*a*) the current in the 100 kΩ resistor in Fig. E.3 and (*b*) the battery voltage *V*.

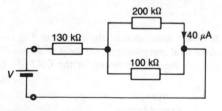

Fig. E.3

1.4 If the current in the 1200 Ω resistor in Fig. E.4 is 5 mA calculate (*a*) the voltage across the 470 Ω resistor, and (*b*) the supply voltage.

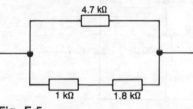

Fig. E.4

1.5 In the circuit given in Fig. E.5 the power dissipated in the 1.8 kΩ resistor is 3 mW. Calculate the total power dissipated in the circuit.

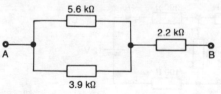

Fig. E.5

1.6 For the circuit shown in Fig. E.6 determine the current that must flow into terminal A to give 5 mA in the 3.9 kΩ resistor. Also calculate the applied voltage.

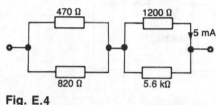

Fig. E.6

1.7 When a power supply is connected across the terminals AB of the circuit in Fig. E.7 the voltage across the 4.7 kΩ resistor is 5 V. Calculate (*a*) the current supplied to the network, and (*b*) the voltage of the supply.

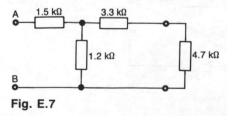

Fig. E.7

1.8 For the circuit shown in Fig. E.8 calculate (*a*) the total resistance connected to the 12 V supply, (*b*) the current in each resistor, and (*c*) the power dissipated in the 3.9 kΩ resistor.

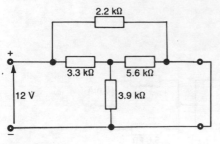

Fig. E.8

1.9 Calculate the current flowing through the 100 Ω resistor in the circuit of Fig. E.9.

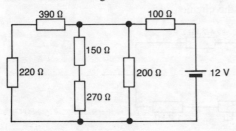

Fig. E.9

1.10 Calculate the current flowing through the 100 Ω resistor in Fig. E.10.

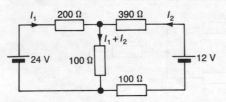

Fig. E.10

1.11 State Kirchhoff's laws. Calculate the current flowing in each of the resistors in Fig. E.11.

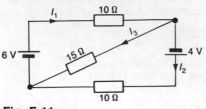

Fig. E.11

1.12 Calculate the current flowing in the 33 Ω resistor in Fig. E.12.

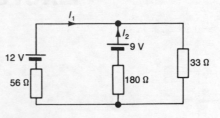

Fig. E.12

Chapter 2

2.1 A capacitor consists of two parallel plates each 10 × 8 cm, separated by a dielectric that is 0.1 mm thick. Calculate its capacitance if $\epsilon_r = 2$.

2.2 A parallel-plate capacitor has ten fixed plates and nine moving plates. The maximum and minimum areas of the spaces between the plates are $40\,cm^2$ and $10\,cm^2$ respectively and the spacing is 0.5 mm. Calculate (*a*) the maximum and minimum values of the capacitance, (*b*) the maximum and minimum charge stored in the capacitor if 10 V is maintained across the plates, and (*c*) the average current that flows into the capacitor if the charge changes from its maximum to its minimum value in 0.2 s.

2.3 Two parallel metal plates are 2 mm apart. If the potential difference across the plates is 50 V what is the electric field strength in the dielectric?

2.4 For the circuit given in Fig. E.13 calculate (*a*) the electric field strength in the capacitor if the plate separation is 0.2 mm, (*b*) the charge stored on the right-hand electrode, and (*c*) the energy stored in the capacitor.

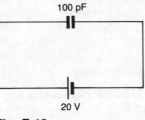

Fig. E.13

2.5 Calculate the total capacitance of the circuit of Fig. E.14. Then find (*a*) the total energy stored, (*b*) the p.d. across each capacitor, and (*c*) the charge stored in the 0.47 μF capacitor.

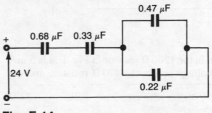

Fig. E.14

2.6 For Fig. E.15 calculate (*a*) the total energy stored, and (*b*) the electric field strength in the 10 μF capacitor if its dielectric is 0.5 mm thick.

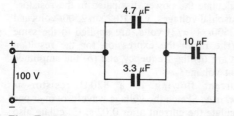

Fig. E.15

2.7 Calculate the charge stored on the plates of a capacitor, each plate having a surface area of 10^4 mm^2, if the electric flux density between the plates is 25 μC/m^2. If the dielectric is 0.1 mm thick and has a relative permittivity of 2.5, calculate the voltage across the capacitor terminals.
2.8 Calculate the capacitance of a parallel plate capacitor whose two plates each have a surface area of 0.05 m^2 and are separated by a 0.01 mm thick dielectric of relative permittivity 2.
2.9 Explain the relationship between two charged bodies and define the meaning of the term relative permittivity. A capacitor is charged at a constant rate of 2.5 mA over a time period of 40 ms after which the capacitor voltage is 12.5 V. Calculate the capacitance of the capacitor.
2.10 A capacitor of 10 μF has a p.d. of 15 V across its terminals. If the electric field strength is 50 kV/m and the flux density is 15 μC/m^2 calculate the dimensions of the capacitor and the relative permittivity of its dielectric.

Chapter 3

3.1 Draw the magnetization curve for the specimen of mild steel whose data is given in Table E.1. From the graph determine the relative permeability of the material when H is 750 A/m. The permeability of free space is $4\pi \times 10^{-7}$ H/m.
3.2 A mild-steel ring is 60 cm long, has a cross-sectional area of 4 cm^2, and a radial air gap of width 1.8 mm. Calculate the m.m.f. necessary to produce a magnetic flux of 300 μWb in the air gap. Use the magnetization curve given in Fig. E.16.
3.3 A conductor carrying a current in the direction into the paper is midway between two permanent magnets. If the left-hand magnet is North and the right-hand magnet is South draw (*a*) the lines of flux, and (*b*) the direction of the force exerted upon the conductor. What would happen if the direction of the current were to be reversed?

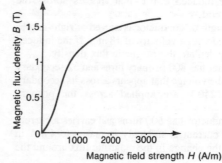

Fig. E.16

3.4 Explain, with the aid of diagrams, how magnetic screening is obtained, (*a*) at low frequencies, and (*b*) at high frequencies.
3.5 State the units of the each of the following magnetic terms and for each of them say what is the electrical equivalent. (*a*) flux density, (*b*) field strength, (*c*) permeability, (*d*) reluctance, and (*e*) m.m.f.
3.6 A coil has 3500 turns of wire wound around a magnetic circuit that is made from silicon steel ($\mu_r - 1030$). The length of the circuit is 16 cm and the current in the coil is 25 mA. Calculate the flux density in the silicon steel.
3.7 Sketch a typical magnetization curve for a magnetic material and mark the saturation region. What does the term magnetic saturation mean?
3.8 A magnetic circuit consists of an 80 cm length of cast iron, having a cross-sectional area of 36 cm^2, and two air gaps each 1.8 mm wide. A coil of wire wound around the iron has 2800 turns and carries a current of 2 A. If the flux produced in the magnetic circuit is 6 mWb calculate the relative permeability of the cast iron.
3.9 Calculate the reluctance of a magnetic circuit that has a cross-sectional area of 1 cm^2 and is wound with 250 turns of wire if, when a current of 1.2 A flows in the coil, a flux density of 0.25 T is set up.
3.10 (*a*) A magnetic material has a magnetic field strength of 1000 A/m and a flux density of 480 mT. Calculate the relative permeability of the material. (*b*) What is the m.m.f. required to produce the above flux density in an air gap of 1 mm width? (*c*) What current must flow in 1000 turns to produce this m.m.f.?

Chapter 4

4.1 A magnetic flux of 600 μWb surrounds a coil of 1200 turns. This flux is reduced to 300 μWb in 2.5 ms. Calculate

Table E.1

Magnetic field strength H (A/m)	250	500	1000	1500	2000	2500	3000
Magentic Flux density B (T)	0.76	1.2	1.58	1.8	1.98	2.1	2.22

the value of the induced e.m.f. that appears across the terminals of the coil.

4.2 A 22 cm length of conductor is moved at right-angles to a magnetic field with a velocity of 18 m/s. If the induced e.m.f. is 1.6 V calculate the magnetic flux density.

4.3 A transformer has 800 primary turns and 32 secondary turns. Calculate the voltage that appears across its secondary terminals when 240 V are applied across the primary terminals.

4.4 A 60 mH inductor has 600 turns and carries a current of 2 mA. If this current is suddenly increased to 4 mA in 100 μs calculate the change in the magnetic flux around the inductor.

4.5 An inductor of 10 mH inductance has a current of 2 A flowing in it. Calculate (a) the e.m.f. induced into the inductor when the current changes to 0.5 A in 100 μs, (b) the energy released by the coil when the current changes.

4.6 A 0.25 m square coil of 300 turns carries a current of 2 A and is situated in a uniform magnetic field of flux density 0.4 T. Calculate the force exerted on the coil.

4.7 (a) A steady magnetic flux of 1 mWb around a 1000-turn coil is reduced to 0.25 mWb in 1 ms. Calculate the e.m.f. induced in the coil. (b) A 40 cm length of conductor is moved with a velocity of 20 m/s at right-angles to a magnetic field. If the induced e.m.f. is then 1 V calculate the flux density of the field.

4.8 A 0.2 m length of conductor moves in a magnetic field with a linear velocity of 100 m/s. The field has a flux density of 0.02 T. Calculate the induced e.m.f. if the direction of movement of the conductor is (a) perpendicular to the field, and (b) at 45° to the direction of the field.

4.9 A transformer has a current of 0.6 A flowing in its primary winding. The secondary voltage across a load of 20 Ω is 12 V. Calculate (a) the turns ratio of the transformer, (b) the number of secondary turns if there are 120 primary turns, and (c) the primary voltage.

4.10 A transformer has 1000 primary turns and 200 secondary turns. The load connected across the secondary terminals is 25 V across 500 Ω. Calculate (a) the primary voltage, (b) the primary current, and (c) the resistance 'seen' looking into the primary terminals.

4.11 A coil has a radius of 1.5 cm and an overall length of 3 cm. The coil has 200 turns and is in a magnetic field of flux density 0.3 T. Calculate the maximum torque developed when a current of 1.8 A flows in the coil.

4.12 A rectangular coil of 50 cm length and 25 cm width has 1200 turns and rotates in a uniform magnetic field about an axis in the plane joining the middle points of the two short sides. The flux density of the magnetic field is 20 mT and it is perpendicular to the axis. If the coil rotates with a uniform velocity of 10 revs/s calculate the e.m.f. generated.

Chapter 5

5.1 Two sinusoidal voltages V_1 and V_2 have amplitudes of 5 V and 8 V respectively and V_2 lags V_1 by 50°. If the frequencies of the two signals are the same determine the amplitude and phase angle, relative to V_1, of the resultant voltage.

5.2 The voltage $v = 25 \sin \omega t$ volts is applied to a resistor of 2200 Ω. Calculate the power dissipated in the resistor.

5.3 Two sinusoidal voltages, $v = 10.2 \sin 2500t$ volts and $v = 15 \sin (2500t + \pi/2)$ volts, are applied to the same resistance. Write down the expression for the resultant voltage. What are (a) the frequency and (b) the amplitude of the resultant voltage?

5.4 The current flowing in a 820 Ω resistor is $i = 4 \sin 200\pi t$ mA. Sketch the voltage waveform over one cycle and calculate the current after 0.02 s. Calculate also the mean voltage and the r.m.s. voltage.

5.5 Write down the expression for a sinusoidal voltage of peak value 100 V and frequency 50 Hz. This voltage is to be applied to a resistor to dissipate a power of 5 W. What value of resistance is needed?

5.6 Draw, on the same graph paper, two cycles of a current of 1 A peak value and frequency 1 kHz and another current of 0.8 A, at the same frequency but leading the first current by 30°.

5.7 Calculate the peak, average and r.m.s. values of the current $282.8 \sin 2000\pi t$ mA. Calculate the value of the current at time $t = 0.6$ ms.

5.8 A sawtooth voltage increases from 0 V to 4 V in 100 μs and then falls back to 0 V in 5 μs. Sketch the waveform and determine its average value.

5.9 A power of 500 mW is dissipated in a 1 kW resistor by a sinusoidal current. Determine the peak value of the current.

5.10 An a.c. voltage of peak value 25 V is applied to a bridge rectifier circuit that has a smoothing capacitor. Neglecting any circuit losses what is the approximate d.c. output voltage of the circuit?

5.11 Two voltage sources acting in series have e.m.f.s given by $v_1 = 100 \sin 100\pi t$ volts and $v_2 = 80 \sin (100\pi t + 45°)$ volts. Draw the phasor diagram of v_1 and v_2 and use it to obtain an expression for the resultant voltage.

Chapter 6

6.1 An a.c. current of 2 mA at 1 kHz flows in a series circuit that consists of a 2.2 kΩ resistor and a 150 mH inductor. Calculate (a) the reactance of the inductor, and (b) the supply voltage and its phase relative to the current. Draw to scale the impedance triangle.

6.2 A capacitor having a reactance of 300 Ω at a frequency of 5 kHz, is connected in series with a 470 Ω resistor. Calculate (a) the capacitance, (b) the current that flows, and (c) the voltage across each component when 25 V at 5 kHz is applied to the circuit. Draw the phasor diagram.

6.3 A series LCR circuit has $L = 25$ mH, $C = 0.2 \mu$F and $R = 50 \Omega$. Calculate (a) the resonant frequency, (b) the Q factor, (c) the resonant current when 2 V at the resonant frequency are applied, and (d) the voltage then across the capacitor.

6.4 The true power in an a.c. circuit is 600 mW. Calculate the apparent power if the power factor is (a) 0.4, and (b) 0.75. Draw to scale the power triangle.

6.5 A current $i = 4.6 \sin 4000t$ amps is applied to (a) a resistor of 120 Ω, (b) an inductor of 20 mH, and (c) a capacitor of 2.2 μF. For each write down the expression for the voltage across the component. What is the power dissipated in each case?

6.6 Write down the expression for the voltage across a pure inductive reactance of 3000 Ω when a current of 10 mA flows in it. Calculate (a) the apparent power, (b) the true power and (c) the reactive volt-amperes.

6.7 Calculate the power dissipated in a 50 μH inductor that is connected to a 3 MHz supply if the current that flows is 1 mA and the self-resistance of the inductor is 1 Ω. Also find the supply voltage.

6.8 A series LCR circuit has $R = 20$ Ω, $L = 1$ mH, and $C = 22$ nF. Calculate (a) the resonant frequency, (b) the power dissipated when the applied voltage is 1 V at the resonant frequency, (c) the Q factor, and (d) the capacitor voltage.

6.9 A series RC circuit has a reactive power of 30 var. If the apparent power is 40 VA calculate the phase angle between the supply voltage and the current. What is the true power? Draw the impedance and power triangles for the circuit.

6.10 A series circuit takes a current of 1.5 A from a 240 V 50 Hz mains supply with a power factor of 0.75 leading. Calculate (a) the circuit component values, and (b) the power dissipated in the circuit.

6.11 An inductor is connected to a 6 V 5 kHz a.c. voltage source when a current of 2.5 mA flows in it. The power dissipated in the inductor is 62 μW. Calculate the resistance and inductance of the inductor.

6.12 A 4.7 kΩ resistor is connected in series with a 10 nF capacitor and a 10 V 3 kHz voltage is applied across the circuit. Calculate (a) the impedance of the circuit, (b) the current that flows, and (c) the power dissipated. Draw the impedance and power triangles of the circuit.

Chapter 7

7.1 With the aid of waveform diagrams illustrate the difference between amplitude-, and frequency-modulation of a sinusoidal carrier. Explain when and why modulation is used.

7.2 A baseband signal of 100–4000 Hz amplitude modulates a 100 kHz carrier. List all the frequencies that are contained in the modulated waveform. What is the minimum bandwidth needed to transmit the modulated wave?

7.3 What is meant by (a) an analogue signal and (b) a digital signal? Give one example of each. Why cannot digital data be transmitted directly over the analogue telephone network? How can digital signals be represented in (i) an a.m. system, and (ii) a f.m. system?

7.4 A complex signal that includes frequencies in the range 50–3000 Hz is to be transmitted over a pcm multi-channel telephony system. What will be the minimum sampling rate?

What is meant by quantization? Why is the number of quantization levels always some multiple of 2?

7.5 With the aid of a waveform sketch explain what is meant by the wavelength of a signal that is propagating from one point to another. A 12 MHz signal is transmitted over a coaxial cable with a velocity 0.85 times the velocity of light. Calculate the wavelength of the signal.

7.6 What is meant by the terms wide area network and local area network when applied to data communication? List four possible network configurations and briefly compare their relative merits. What is meant by a protocol and why is the use of one necessary in a data system? Give outline details of two typical protocols.

7.7 Data signals may be transmitted using either a parallel or a serial format. Discuss the relative merits of the two formats and say when each would be employed. Serial signals may be transmitted using either non-synchronous or synchronous methods; give an example of each and state their relative merits.

7.8 The signal shown in Fig. E.17 is sampled at times a, b, c, d, e, and f. Show the binary-coded representation of each sample and then draw the pcm signal thus produced.

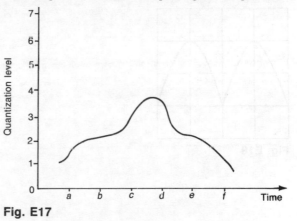

Fig. E17

7.9 Draw the serial digital data signal that represents the binary number 10110010. State the use of the most significant bit. If the signal is transmitted non-synchronously start and stop bits will be used; show where they are included in the signal and explain how they act to provide the necessary synchronization at the receiver.

7.10 (a) List the various systems that are available for the transmission of information by electrical means. Briefly discuss their relative merits. (b) What is the essential difference between a d.c. signal and an a.c. signal and why are the applications for the former rather limited? (c) A d.c data signal can be transmitted over a line by making use of either modems or pulse regenerators. Outline the principle of each method.

Chapter 8

8.1 A moving-coil meter has a self-resistance of 25 Ω and needs a current of 6 mA to flow for fsd. Calculate (a) the shunt resistance for the instrument to read up to 1 A, and (*b*) the multiplier resistance to give the instrument a range of 1−50 V. What are the desirable properties of the shunt and multiplier resistances?

8.2 The current in (*a*) a circuit containing only resistances supplied by a d.c. voltage source, (*b*) the same circuit supplied by an a.c. voltage source at a frequency of 12 kHz, is to be measured. Moving-coil, moving-iron and thermodynamic meters are available. State, with reasons, which instrument should be used for each measurement.

8.3 The resistance of a coil is to be measured using the ammeter/voltmeter method. Sketch the circuit to be used when the resistance is (*a*) high, and (*b*) low. If the coil resistance is exactly 10 Ω and the ammeter and voltmeter resistances are 0.6 Ω and 20 kΩ respectively, calculate the percentage error in the measurement in each case.

8.4 The display shown in Fig. E.18 was obtained on a cro with the sensitivities of the Y channel and the timebase set to 5 V/cm and 200 μs/cm respectively. Calculate the periodic time, the frequency, the peak voltage, the average voltage and the r.m.s. voltage of the signal.

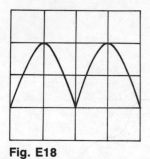

Fig. E18

8.5 (*a*) With the aid of sketches describe the principle of operation of a moving-iron meter. (*b*) Why is the meter suitable for both a.c. and d.c. measurements (*c*) Why is the scale of the meter non-linear? (*d*) How can the (i) current range, (ii) voltage range of the meter be increased?

8.6 What is meant by a *null* method of measurement and what are its advantages? Describe the operation of a Wheatstone bridge and derive the balance equations. In a particular measurement balance was obtained when the ratio resistances were of equal value and the variable resistance was set to 1237 Ω. Calculate the value of the unknown resistance.

8.7 (*a*) With the aid of sketches describe the operation of a moving-coil meter. (*b*) Answer the following questions: (i) is the scale non-linear? (ii) can a.c. currents be measured? (*c*) Show how a bridge rectifier unit can be added to allow a.c. measurements. Can the instrument then read d.c. currents?

8.8 (*a*) Draw the circuit diagram of an ohm meter and describe how it works. What are the functions of the fixed and the variable resistors in the meter? Must they always be in the same positions? (*b*) Discuss the relative merits of analogue and digital voltmeters.

8.9 A moving coil meter has a resistance of 50 Ω and a fsd current of 0.5 mA. A shunt is used to enable the meter to read currents of up to 2 A. Calculate the power dissipated in the meter when the meter indicates 2 A.

8.10 A circuit consists of three resistors connected in series across a 100 V d.c. supply. The values of the resistors are 4.7 kΩ, 3.3 kΩ and 5.6 kΩ. The voltage across the 5.6 kΩ resistor is to be measured using (*a*) a moving-coil meter whose resistance is 20 kΩ, and (*b*) an electronic voltmeter whose resistance is 1 MΩ. Calculate the percentage error in each measurement.

Answers to numerical exercises

1.1 $12\,k\|12\,k\|3\,k = 1/[1/12 + 1/12 + 1/3] = 2\,k\Omega$.
$6.2\|3.9 = (6.6 \times 3.9)/(6.2 + 3.9) = 2.39\,k\Omega$.
Total $R = 1.6 + 2 + 2.39 \simeq 6\,k\Omega$.
(a) $I_s = 24/6000 = 4\,mA$.
(b) $I_{3.9} = 4 \times 6.2/(6.2 + 3.9) = 2.46\,mA$.
(c) $I_{6.2} = 4 - 2.46 = 1.54\,mA$. $P = (1.54 \times 10^{-3})^2 \times 6.2 \times 10^3 3 = 14.7\,mW$.

1.2 (a) $P = 100/(8.2 \times 10^3) = 12.2\,mW$.
(b) $V_{2.2} = 10 \times 2.2/14.2 = 1.55\,V$.
(c) $I_{8.2} = 10/8.2 = 1.22\,mA$.
$I_{12} = I_{2.2} = 10/14.2 = 0.7\,mA$.
$I_s = 1.22 + 0.7 = 1.92\,mA$.

1.3 (a) $V_{200} = 40 \times 10^{-6} \times 200 \times 10^3 = 8\,V$.
$I_{100} = 8/100 \times 10^3 = 80\,\mu A$.
(b) $V_{130} = 120 \times 10^{-6} \times 130 \times 10^3 = 15.6\,V$. $V = 23.6\,V \simeq 24\,V$.

1.4 (a) $V_{1.2} = 5 \times 10^{-3} \times 1200 = 6\,V$. $I_{5.6} = 6/5.6 = 1.07\,mA$.
$I_s = 5 + 1.07 = 6.07\,mA$. $470\|820 = 299\,\Omega$.
$V_{470} = 6.07 \times 10^{-3} \times 299 = 1.82\,V$.
(b) $V_s = 6 + 1.82 = 7.82\,V$.

1.5 $3 \times 10^{-3} = I_{1.8}^2 \times 1800$, $I_{1.8} = 1.29\,mA$. $P_1 = (1.29 \times 10^{-3})^2 \times 1000 = 1.664\,mW$. $V_{4.7} = 1.29 \times 2.8 = 3.612\,V$. $P_{4.7} = 3.612^2/(4.7 \times 10^3) = 2.776\,mW$. Total power $= 1.664 + 3 + 2.776 = 7.44\,mW$.

1.6 $5 = I_s \times 5.6/(5.6 + 3.9) = 0.59\,I_s$, $I_s = 8.48\,mA$.
$5.6\|3.9 = 2.3\,k\Omega$, $R = 2.2 + 2.3 = 4.5\,k\Omega$. $V_s = 4.5 \times 8.48 = 38.2\,V$.

1.7 (a) $I_{4.7} = 5/4.7 = 1.064\,mA$. $V_{1.2} = 1.064 \times (3.3 + 4.7) = 8.51\,V$. $I_{1.2} = 8.51/1200 = 7.092\,mA$. $I_s = 1.064 + 7.09 = 8.16\,mA$.
(b) $V_{1.5} = 8.16 \times 1.5 = 12.24\,V$. $V_s = 12.24 + 8.512 \simeq 20\,V$.

1.8 (a) $3.9\|5.6 = 2.3\,k\Omega$. $3.3 + 2.3 = 5.6\,k\Omega$.
$R = (2.2 \times 5.6)/(2.2 + 5.6) = 1.58\,k\Omega$.
(b) $I_s = 12/1.58 = 7.6\,mA$. $I_{2.2} = (7.6 \times 5.6)/(5.6 + 2.2) = 5.46\,mA$.
$I_{3.3} = 7.6 - 5.46 = 2.14\,mA$.
$I_{3.9} = (2.14 \times 5.6)/(5.6 + 3.9) = 1.26\,mA$.
$I_{5.6} = 2.14 - 1.26 = 0.88\,mA$.
(c) $P_{3.9} = (1.26 \times 10^{-3})^2 \times 3.9 \times 10^3 = 6.2\,mW$.

1.9 $220 + 390 = 610\,\Omega$. $150 + 270 = 420\,\Omega$. $1/R_p = 1/610 + 1/420 + 1/200$. $R_p = 110.9\,\Omega \simeq$
$111\,\Omega$. $I_s = 12/211 = 56.87\,mA$.

1.10 $24 = 200\,I_1 + 100(I_1 + I_2)$, $I_2 = (24 - 300\,I_1)/100$.
$12 = 100(I_1 + I_2) + (390 + 100)I_2 = 100\,I_1 + 5.9(24 - 300\,I_1)$. $I_1 = 77.6\,mA$. Also, $I_2 = (24 - 300 \times 77.6 \times 10^{-3})/100 = 7.2\,mA$. $I = 84.8\,mA$.

1.11 $6 = 10\,I_1 + 15(I_1 - I_2)$. $I_1 = (6 + 15\,I_2)/25$.
$4 = 10\,I_2 - 15(I_1 - I_2)$, $I_1 = (4 + 25\,I_2)/15$.
Equating, $I_1 = 525\,mA$, $I_2 = 475\,mA$, and $I_3 = -50\,mA$.

1.12 $12 = 56\,I_1 + 33(I_1 + I_2) = 89\,I_1 + 33\,I_2$.
$9 = 180\,I_2 + 33(I_1 + I_2) = 213\,I_2 + 33\,I_1$.
Solving, $I_{33} = 149\,mA$.

2.1 $C = (8.854 \times 10^{-12} \times 2 \times 80 \times 10^{-4})/(0.1 \times 10^{-3}) = 1.42\,nF$.

2.2 (a) $C_{max} = (8.854 \times 10^{-12} \times 40 \times 10^{-4} \times 18)/(0.5 \times 10^{-3}) = 1.27\,nF$.
$C_{min} = C_{max}/4 = 0.32\,nF$.
(b) $Q_{max} = C_{max}\,V = 1.27 \times 10 = 12.27\,nC$.
$Q_{min} = Q_{max}/4 = 3.2\,nC$.
(c) $I_{av} = Q_{av}/t = 7.735/0.2 = 38.7\,nA$.

2.3 $E = 50/(2 \times 10^{-3}) = 25\,kV/m$.

2.4 (a) $E = 20/(0.2 \times 10^{-3}) = 100\,kV/m$.
(b) $Q = CV = 100 \times 10^{-12} \times 20 = 2\,nC$.
(c) $E = CV^2/2 = 100 \times 10^{-12} \times 400 \times 0.5 = 20\,nJ$.

2.5 $0.47\|0.22 = 0.69\,\mu F$. $1/C_T = (1/0.68 + 1/0.33 + 1/0.69)$, $C_T = 0.168\,\mu F$.
(a) $E = 0.168 \times 10^{-6} \times 24^2 \times 0.5 = 48.38\,\mu J$.
(b) $Q = CV = 0.168 \times 10^{-6} \times 24 = 4\,\mu C$.
$V_1 = 4/0.68 = 5.88\,V$.
$V_2 = 4/0.33 = 12.12\,V$. $V_3 = 4/0.69 = 5.8\,V$.
(c) $Q_{0.47} = 0.47 \times 10^{-6} \times 5.8 = 2.73\,\mu C$.

2.6 (a) $4.7\|3.3 = 8\,\mu F$. $C_T = (8 \times 10)/(8 + 10) = 4.44\,\mu F$. $E = 4.44 \times 10^{-6} \times 10^4 \times 0.5 = 22.2\,mJ$.
(b) $V_{10} = (100 \times 8)/(10 + 8) = 44.44\,V$.
$E = 44.4/(0.5 \times 10^{-3}) = 88.89\,kV/m$.

2.7 $Q = DA = 25 \times 10^{-6} \times 10^4 \times 10^{-6} = 250\,nC$.
$D = \epsilon_0\epsilon_r E$, $E = (25 \times 10^{-6})/(8.854 \times 10^{-12} \times 2.5) = 1.13\,MV/m$.
$E = V/d = 1.13 \times 10^6 \times 0.1 \times 10^{-3} = 113\,V$.

2.8 $C = (8.854 \times 10^{-12} \times 2 \times 0.05)/(0.01 \times 10^{-3}) = 88.5$ nF.

2.9 $Q = 2.5 \times 10^{-3} \times 40 \times 10^{-3} = 100\,\mu$C.
$C = Q/V = 8\,\mu$F.

2.10 $50 \times 10^3 = 15/d$. $d = 0.3$ mm.
$15 \times 10^{-3} = Q/A = VC/A$.
$A = (15 \times 10 \times 10^{-6})/(15 \times 10^{-3}) = 0.01$ m^2. $\epsilon_T = D/\epsilon_0 = 3.39$

3.1 See Fig. A.1. From this at $H = 750$ A/m $B = 1.4$ T. $\mu_r = B/\mu_0 H = 1.4/(4\pi \times 10^{-7} \times 750) = 1485$.

3.2 $B = \phi/A = (300 \times 10^{-6})/(C4 \times 10^{-4}) = 0.75$ T.
From curve at $B = 0.75$ $H = 600$ A/m. For mild steel $F = Hl = 600 \times 0.5982 = 359$ A.
For air gap $H = B/\mu_0 = 0.75(4\pi \times 10^{-7}) = 0.597 \times 10^6$ A/m. $F = 0.597 \times 10^6 \times 1.8 \times 10^{-3} = 1075$ A. m.m.f $= 359 + 1075 = 1434$ A.

3.6 $B = \mu NI/l = (1030 \times 4\pi \times 10^{-7} \times 3500 \times 25 \times 10^{-3})/(16 \times 10^{-2}) = 0.71$ T.

3.8 $F = NI = 2800 \times 2 = 5600$ A. $S_T = F/\phi = 5600/(6 \times 10^{-3}) = 933.3 \times 10^3\,H^{-1}$. $S_A = l/\mu A = (2 \times 1.8 \times 10^{-3})/(4\pi \times 10^{-7} \times 36 \times 10^{-4}) = 795.8 \times 10^3\,H^{-1}$.
$S_I = S_T - S_A = (933.3 - 795.8) \times 10^3 = 137.5 \times 10^3\,H^{-1}$.
$\mu_r = l/S_I \mu_0 A = (76.4 \times 10^{-2})/(4\pi \times 10^{-7} \times 36 \times 10^{-4} \times 137.5 \times 10^3) = 1228$.

3.9 $\phi = BA = 0.25 \times 10^{-4} = 25\,\mu$Wb. m.m.f. $= NI = 250 \times 1.2 = 300$ A.

$S = $ m.m.f.$/\phi = 300/(25 \times 10^{-6}) = 12 \times 10^6\,H^{-1}$.

3.10 (a) $\mu_r = 0.48/(4\pi \times 10^{-7} \times 1000) = 382$.
(b) $H = B/\mu_0 = 0.48/(4\pi \times 10^{-7}) = 381\,972$.
m.m.f. $= H \times 1 \times 10^{-3} = 382$ A.
(c) $I = 382/1000 = 382$ mA.

4.1 $E = -N\,d\phi/dt = -1200 \times (300 \times 10^{-6})/(2.5 \times 10^{-3}) = -144$ V.

4.2 $B = E/lv = 1.6/(22 \times 10^{-2} \times 18) = 0.404$ T.

4.3 $V_s = 240 \times 32/800 = 9.6$ V.

4.4 $E = L\,di/dt = (60 \times 10^{-3} \times 2 \times 10^{-3})/(100 \times 10^{-6}) = 1.2$ V.
$E = N\,d\phi/dt$. $d\phi = E\,dt/N = (1.2 \times 100 \times 10^{-6})/600 = 0.2\,\mu$Wb.

4.5 (a) $E = (10 \times 10^{-3} \times 1.5)/(100 \times 10^{-6}) = 150$ V.
(b) Energy released $= 10 \times 10^{-3}(2^2 - 0.5^2)/2 = 18.75$ mJ.

4.6 $F = BIl = 0.4 \times 2 \times 2 \times 0.25 \times 300 = 120$ N.

4.7 (a) $E = -(1000 \times 0.75 \times 10^{-3})/(1 \times 10^{-3}) = 750$ V.
(b) $B = E/lv = 1/(40 \times 10^{-2} \times 20) = 0.125$ T.

4.8 (a) $E = Blv = 0.02 \times 0.2 \times 100 = 0.4$ V.
(b) $E = Blv \sin\theta = 0.4 \sin 45° = 0.283$ V.

4.9 (a) $I_s = 12/200 = 0.06$ A. $n = 0.06/0.6 = 1{:}10$.
(b) $N_s = 10 \times 120 = 1200$.
(c) $V_p = 12/10 = 1.2$ V.

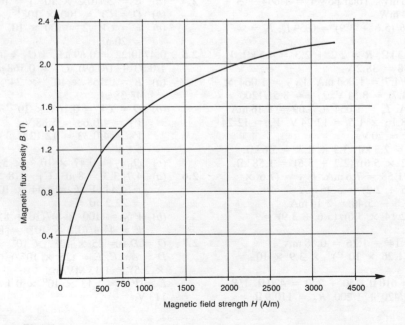

Fig. A1

4.10 $n = 5{:}1$, $I_s = 25/500 = 50$ mA.
(a) $V_p = 5 \times 25 = 125$ V.
(b) $I_p = 50/5 = 10$ mA.
(c) $R_p = 125/10 = 12.5$ kΩ, or $R_p = 25 \times 500$
$= 12.5$ kΩ.

4.11 $T = 2NBIlr$ Nm $= 2 \times 200 \times 0.3 \times 1.8 \times 3$
$\times 10^{-2} \times 1.5 \times 10^{-2} = 0.097$ Nm.

4.12 $v = 2\pi rf$. $E = BlvN = 0.02 \times 2 \times 0.5 \times 2\pi$
$\times 0.125 \times 10 \sin\theta \times 1200 = 188.5 \sin\theta$ V.

5.1 Resolving the 8 V signal gives $8 \sin 45° = 8 \cos$
$45° = 5.66$ V.
Hence, $|V_T| = \sqrt{[(5 + 5.66)^2 + 5.66^2]} =$
12.07 V. $\phi = \tan^{-1}(5.66/10.66) = 28°$.
Therefore, $|V_T| = 12.07 \angle 28°$ V.

5.2 $P = (25/\sqrt2)^2/2200 = 142.1$ mW.

5.3 $|V| = \sqrt{(10.2^2 + 15^2)} = 18.14$ V. $\angle\phi =$
$\tan^{-1}(15/10.2) = 55.8°$.
$v = 18.14 \sin (2500t + 55.8°)$ volts.
(a) $f = 398$ Hz.
(b) $V = 18.14$ V.

5.4 $v = 4 \times 0.82 \sin (200\pi \times 0.02) = 0$ V.
$V_{av} = 3.28 \times 0.637 = 2.09$ V.
$V = 3.28 \times 0.707 = 2.32$ V.

5.5 $5 = (100/\sqrt2)^2/R = 1000$ Ω.

5.7 $i = 282.2$ mA, $I_{av} = 282.8 \times 0.637 = 180$ mA,
$I = 282.8 \times 0.707 = 200$ mA.
$i = 282.8 \sin (2000\pi \times 0.6 \times 10^{-3}) =$
-166.2 mA.

5.8 $V_{av} = 2$ V.

5.9 $P = 0.5 = 1000I^2$. $I = \sqrt{(0.5/1000)} =$
22.36 mA. $I_m = \sqrt2 I = 31.62$ mA.

5.10 25 V.

5.11 $V = \sqrt{[(100 + 80 \cos 45°)^2 + (80 \sin 45°)^2]} =$
166.5 V.
$\phi = \tan^{-1}(56.56/156.56) = 19.9 \simeq 20°$.
Therefore, $v = 166.5 \sin (100\pi t + 20°)$ volts.

6.1 (a) $\omega L = 2\pi \times 10^3 \times 150 \times 10^{-3} = 943$ Ω.
(b) $Z = \sqrt{[(2.2 \times 10^3)^2 + 943^2)]} = 2394$ Ω.
$\phi = \tan^{-1}(943/2200) = 23.32°$. $V_s = IZ =$
4.8 V $\angle 23.2°$ V.

6.2 (a) $X_c = 300 = 1/(2\pi \times 5000C)$, $C = 0.1$ μF.
(b) $|Z| = \sqrt{(470^2 + 300^2)} = 557.6$ Ω.
$\phi = \tan^{-1}(-300/470) = -32.6°$.
$I = 25/557.6 \angle -32.6° =$
$44.84 \angle +32.6°$ mA.
(c) $V_R = 470I = 21.08 \angle 32.6°$ V.
$V_c = 300 \angle -90° \times I =$
$13.45 \angle -57.4°$ V.

6.3 (a) $f_0 = 1/2\pi \sqrt{[(25 \times 10^{-3} \times 0.2 \times 10^{-6})]} =$
2251 Hz.
(b) $Q = 0.02 \sqrt{[(25 \times 10^{-3})/(0.2 \times 10^{-6})]} =$
7.07.
(c) $I_0 = 2/50 = 40$ mA.
(d) $V_c = QE = 7.07 \times 2 = 14.14$ V.

6.4 (a) 600 mW $= 0.4P$, $P = 1.5$ VA.
(b) 600 mW $= 0.75P$, $P = 800$ mVA.

6.5 (a) $v = 552 \sin 4000t$ V.
(b) $\omega L = 4000 \times 20 \times 10^{-3} = 80$ Ω.
$v = 368 \sin (4000t + 90°)$ V.
(c) $1/\omega C = 1/(4000 \times 2.2 \times 10^{-6}) =$
113.64 Ω.
$v = 522 \sin (4000t - 90°)$ V.
$P_R = (552/\sqrt2)^2/120 = 1270$ W. $P_C = P_L$
$= 0$.

6.6 $v = 30 \sin (\omega t + 90°)$ V.
(a) App. power $= VI = 30 \times 10 \times 10^{-3} =$
0.3 VA.
(b) True power $= VI \cos 90° = 0$.
(c) Reactive volt-amps $= VI \sin 90° = 0.3$ var.

6.7 $P = (1 \times 10^{-3})^2 \times 1 = 1$ μW.
$X_L = 2\pi \times 3 \times 10^6 \times 50 \times 10^{-6} = 942.5$ Ω.
$Z \simeq X_L$, so $V_s = 1 \times 10^{-3} \times 942.5 =$
0.943 V.

6.8 (a) $f_0 = 1/2\pi \sqrt{(1 \times 10^{-3} \times 22 \times 10^{-9})} =$
33.932 kHz.
(b) $I_0 = 1/20 = 50$ mA. $P = (50 \times 10^{-3})^2 \times$
$20 = 50$ mW.
(c) $Q = (1/R)(\sqrt{L/C}) = 0.05 \sqrt{[(1 \times 10^{-3})/$
$(22 \times 10^{-9})]} = 10.7$.
(d) $V_c = QE = 10.7 \times 1 = 10.7$ V.

6.9 $40 = VI$, $30 = VI \sin\phi$, $\sin\phi = 30/40 = 0.75$.
$\phi = 48.6°$.
$P = 40 \cos 48.6° = 26.45$ W.

6.10 Since the p.f. is leading the circuit is R in series
with C.
$|Z| = V/I = 240/1.5 = 160$ Ω. p.f. $= \cos\phi =$
R/Z,
$R = 0.75 \times 160 = 120$ Ω.
$X_c = \sqrt{(160^2 - 120^2)} = 105.83$ Ω. $C = 1/(100\pi$
$\times 105.83) = 30$ μF.

6.11 $Z = 6/(2.5 \times 10^{-3}) = 2400$ Ω. $P = I^2R$,
$R = (62 \times 10^{-6})/(2.5 \times 10^{-3})^2 = 9.92$ Ω.
$X_L \simeq Z = 2400$ Ω. $L = 2400/(2\pi \times 5000) =$
76.4 mH.

6.12 $X_c = 5305$ Ω. (a) $Z = \sqrt{(4700^2 + 5305^2)} =$
7088 Ω.
$\phi = \tan^{-1}(-5305/4700) = -48.5°$. $Z =$
$7088 \angle -48.5°$.
(b) $I = V/Z = 1.41 \angle 48.5$ mA.
(c) $P = VI \cos\phi = 10 \times 1.41 \times 10^{-3} \cos$
$48.5° = 9.34$ mW.

7.2 96 to 99.9 kHz, 100 kHz, 100.1 to 104 kHz. $B =$
8 kHz.

7.4 6 kHz.

7.5 $\lambda = v/f = (0.85 \times 3 \times 10^8)/(12 \times 10^6) =$
21.25 m.

8.1 (a) $V_m = 6 \times 10^{-3} \times 25 = 0.15$ V. $I_s = 1 -$
$(6 \times 10^{-3}) = 0.994$ A.
$R_s = 0.15/0.994 = 0.1509$ Ω.
(b) $50 - 0.15 = 49.85$ V. $R_m = 49.85/(6 \times$
$10^{-3}) = 8308$ Ω.

8.3 (a) $R = 0.6 + (10 \times 20k)/(10 + 20k) =$

$10.595 \ \Omega$. $I = V/10.595$, $V = I \times 9.995 =$ 0.9434 V. Measured $R = 0.9434 \times 10.595$ $= 9.995 \ \Omega$.

Percentage error $= [(9.995 - 10)/10] \times 100 = -0.05\%$.

(b) $I = V/10.6$. Measured $R = V/(V/10.6) = 10.6 \ \Omega$.

Percentage error $= [(10.6 - 10)/10] \times 100 = +6\%$.

8.4 $T = 2 \ \text{cm} = 400 \ \mu\text{s}$.

$f = 1/T = 2500 \ \text{Hz}$.

Peak-to-peak voltage $= 2 \ \text{cm} = 10 \ \text{V}$. Therefore, $V_\text{m} = 5 \ \text{V}$, $V_\text{av} = 5 \times 0.637 = 3.185 \ \text{V}$, and $V = 5 \times 0.707 = 3.535 \ \text{V}$.

8.6 $R_\text{x} = 1237 \ \Omega$.

8.9 $P_\text{m} = (0.5 \times 10^{-3})^2 \times 50 = 12.5 \ \mu\text{W}$. $P_\text{s} = 1.9995^2 \times 0.0125 = 49.975 \ \text{mW}$.

Total power $= 49.99 \ \text{mW}$.

$[2^2 \times 0.0125 = 50 \ \text{mW}.]$

8.10 True voltage $= (100 \times 5.6)/13.6 = 41.18 \ \text{V}$.

(a) $5.6\|20 = 4.375 \ \text{k}\Omega$. Measured voltage $= (100 \times 4.375)/12.375 = 35.35 \ \text{V}$.

Percentage error $= [(35.35 - 41.18)/41.18] \times 100 = -14.15\%$.

(b) $5.6k\|1M = 5.569 \ \text{k}\Omega$. Measured voltage $= [(100 \times 5.569)/13.569)] = 41.04 \ \text{V}$.

Percentage error $= [(41.04 - 41.48)/41.48] \times 100 = -0.34\%$.

Index